C000246934

Soho Society

Soho Society

BERNIE KATZ

Foreword by
STEPHEN FRY

Quartet

First published in 2008 by Quartet Books Limited
A member of the Namara Group
27 Goodge Street, London W1T 2LD

A catalogue record for this book is
available from the British Library

ISBN   978 0 7043 7149 1

Art photography
by Unlock Collective
Typeset by Antony Gray
Printed and bound in Spain
by Estudios Gráficos ZURE

I would like to dedicate this book to
the memory of Angus Fairhurst,
a truly great artist.

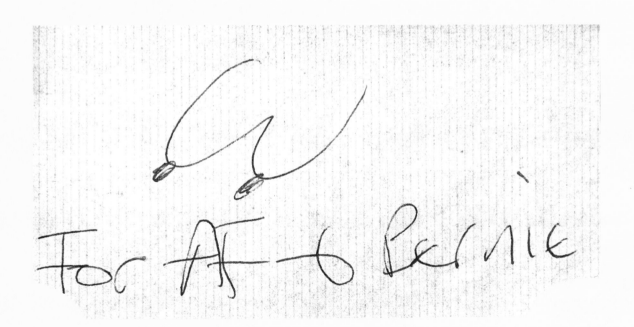

Contents

List of Illustrations

'Give me the lifetime of a butterfly'

anonymous

Foreword

I have collected Soho literature for thirty years. For the last ten or fifteen I had despaired of ever hearing a new voice who *got* it, who really understood what Soho is. And now Bernie Katz has produced this collection and I am happy.

Soho's public face of drugs, prostitution and seedy Bohemia (and yes, they are all to be found in the following pages) has always hidden a private soul of family, neighbourhood, kindness, warmth and connection, and those qualities shine through doggedly. The town centres of Nottingham say, or Bristol, are tougher, harder, crueller and more hostile than the unique parcel of London that is bounded by Shaftesbury Avenue, Oxford Street, Charing Cross Road and Piccadilly.

Not that one should be sentimental about Soho, and Bernie never is. Suffering, failure, sickness, despair and loneliness are found here too. One of the pleasures of buying this book lies in the knowledge that a percentage of its profits will go to help Soho's weakest and most vulnerable.

An established local figure himself, known and loved by all true Soho *habitués*, Bernie is Dean Street's premier ornament, his personality radiates the fun, frolic, sympathy, naughtiness, warmth and energy that characterise the neighbourhood. His writing is a perfect extension of that personality – keen, observant, subtle and above all engaged, fully engaged in the business of seeing and feeling.

Stephen Fry

Bernie Katz

My name is Bernie Katz; I am also known as the Prince of Soho. I was born in Dulwich Hospital in August 1968, the year of the monkey, to an archetypal Jewish mother, forever cleaning and making chicken soup, and a gangster father, whose life ended somewhat abruptly with a bullet in his head.

So used was I to a life of drive-by shootings, I thought nothing of the sound of that gunshot, except for being irritated that it intruded upon my viewing of *The Price Is Right* and came just as Dan Harding from Harlow in Essex was maniacally approaching the stage to whoops and cheers, having beaten off the evening's competition. My only regret that fateful night – which changed my life as I knew it – was that I never found out whether Dan won the three-piece suite with washable covers or the Ford Fiesta.

When I went to investigate, I discovered that thanks to the bullet through his head, my dad's brains were splattered across the four walls of his bedroom. Never one to miss an opportunity, I sashayed over to his wardrobe and navigated my way across the sea of footwear to his black Pierre Cardin alligator-skin shoes, which I'd secretly always had my eye on. Thank God they were in the wardrobe. You see, something good always comes out of any tragedy . . .

As I left the room in my new shoes, I looked back and thought, 'Pa, you've never looked better.'

When the police arrived, they asked me if there was anything I needed. I raised my eyes slowly, as Audrey Hepburn had done after donning her alligator shoes prior to her visit to Sing Sing with the weather report, and chirpily enquired: 'Did any of you happen to catch the end of *The Price Is Right* tonight?'

Now fast forward three years to when I had my first taste of Soho, a place whose image is based on gossip. Take it from me, what you're about to read is not. How do I know? Because I saw all of it with my own eyes. In these stories, you'll get my perspective on Soho. And you'll also get a take on Soho from some of the world's most prolific contemporary artists, whose work adorns the pages of this book. At every turn, you'll meet some of the good, the bad and the ugly (in every sense) who have over the past twenty years, during my reign as Prince of Soho, festooned my life.

You might have met me or just heard of me if you work, rest or play in Soho, but if you haven't, to give you an inkling of what I am about, I'm the man who will help you raise money to build a church. But I'm the same man who would burn it down if the necessity arose! And beware ladies; while you're downstairs re-applying your make-up and I'm out and about, your husband or boyfriend might, at the very same moment, be upstairs banging one out for me while I smoke a fag out of the window.

So why not put your glad rags on and misbehave with me in the playground that is Soho? A word to the wise, however. Leave your man at home and your black alligator-skin shoes under lock and key, because one way or another, I'll get my grubby little hands on both.

Triana Terry – Portrait of Bernie

Marc Quinn – Portrait of Landscapes

Opening Night

Like all places where an abundance of people from all walks of life act out their parallel and intertwining lives, there is a light side and a dark side to Soho.

Let us begin back in the 1990s. It is the opening of the latest in-place; anyone who is anyone or wants to be must be there. But this place is all but impossible to get into. There's a Glaswegian door whore doing a good impersonation of a Rottweiler clutching her guest-list. Standing alongside her is a doorman who looks like a Greek WWF reject. They are fighting with a crowd of people who were meant to be inside this latest hotspot at least an hour ago.

Once inside though, the hassle of getting past those two will soon be a distant memory because the place itself is a work of art, with an art-deco ballroom much more New York than London and a grand sweeping staircase that affords you an overview of the reception hall and the largest chandelier London has ever seen outside of a real palace.

A warning – this Pleasure Palace, like all the others, has a shelf life. This clientele's loyalty begins and ends with its dealer. After the big bang of opening, places like this have nowhere to go but down.

Perhaps this palace will be different. London has been through a few years of economic decline, but now things are looking up, there's money flying around and the acrid whiff of chemicals in the air. This place is unlike anything seen before, better even than when it opened in the 1920s. Perhaps it is the opening night of a new era in the history of London's nightlife; perhaps it is also the beginning of the end for some of those involved.

But for tonight, it's all about fun; dressing up is suddenly back: big hair, high heels, cleavage, sharp dressing and that's just the boys. Of course, these days it's no longer chic to be so groomed. To be cool you have to look a little ragged, hair is best worn after being dragged through a hedge.

Remember this place was just one step away from a members' club, and Soho is full of them today. Soho is home to the members' club.

Once inside and down that incredible staircase there is a large reception area beyond which are two grand rooms, one of them a cocktail bar with the best-looking barmen, mixing drinks and searching for beds for the night – anything so long as they don't have to go home on the N53. People everywhere are checking themselves in the mirrors and checking out potential passions in the room. The bar itself looks like it may have come out of the SS *Normandie*: deco deluxe.

Leaving the sideshow we enter the big top, the restaurant, the second of the two grand rooms. It's a huge decadent space with booths the size of small bedrooms and just as intimate. At the time it boasts the longest bar in town, original artwork dominates the panelled walls, marble pillars hold the ceiling forty feet from the ground.

All in all, this particular opening night is a success to the eye.

Mind you, behind the scenes there's a completely different story. The Rottweiller and the Greek wrestler have been given the wrong guest-list by a totally inexperienced PR girl, just out of university, and out of her depth. Phone lines are down and the fax machine has given up. There are three people working on reception. One is OD-ing. The other two are off their heads on Colombia's finest, hysterical over a missing kilo of the stuff; no good can come of that. The fate of the crowd's belongings is in the hands of these gods, except in this place there are no gods – only the Devil is at work.

The waiters barely speak to each other, they are either having a domestic or they've just realised the guy they picked up last night at Substation is their 'commis'. Behind the counter, the straight boys have commandeered the bar for their hunting ground, as usual, and are working it hard. Their bait is the cocktails that they mix. In the kitchen all hell is breaking loose because the *maître d'* is being throttled by the chef; he never did make it that night to his reservation board. The sharpest waiters have to take over the helm.

Vinnie, the smartest of all, being hip to these facts, appears to be spinning out of control – always a good tactic – but is in fact steering this ship. Through a fire exit, he slips six friends into the best of the booths, held back for the most important of the VIPs. There they remain all night long, eating and drinking, with frequent trips to use that special little shelf so thoughtfully provided in each toilet cubicle. After five hours the bill comes, one bottle of Pinot and a couple of entrées – sixty quid. Great value, they all exclaim, heading to the reception. They get their coats, give the girls, who look strangely terrified, a generous tip and flee into the night through the front door, past a crowd still outside longing to get in, to become part of Sodom and Gomorrah's last stand.

Six months later this same waiter comes stumbling out of Tom's. It's 8 a.m. and his shift starts at 8.30. No longer is he at the Pacific. After five months there, and a month of cold turkey on a friend's sofa, he is working at the Club. While grabbing a coffee at the twenty-four-hour coffee bar, unchanged since 1954, he bumps into an old friend. Too exhausted to be shocked, Vinnie tells this friend where he's off to.

'Funny, I have a breakfast meeting there with Aran Greenshaw, a producer,' comes the reply.

'Oh, don't worry, I know Aran. Come on, let's go. We can walk together . . .'

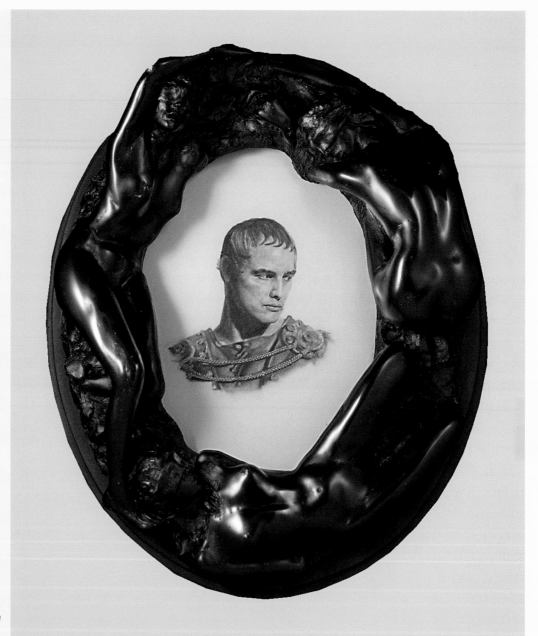

Nina Fowler – Mark Antony

The Hunt

The origin of the word Soho, as you may know, comes from the old hunting cry of King Henry VIII. In the days when the area was open countryside with plenty of game, one would cry 'So-ho!' to call off the hounds. By 1600, when the land began to be urbanised, the whole area had taken this term as its name, Soho. Today a replica of Henry's hunting lodge conceals rather improbably an electrical transformer substation in the middle of Soho Square.

This square was laid out in 1681 when wealthy merchants built grand houses around its perimeter, each trying to outdo the next. Charles II, by then on the throne, had a statue commissioned in the same year which originally stood in the centre of the square. It passed into private ownership but was returned and erected on the north side in 1938.

By the mid-eighteenth century, Soho Square and its environs contained the most magnificent places of public entertainment in Europe. One such, Carlisle House, even became the template for all those members' clubs that came after, and are still coming. The hostess, a European opera singer, created perhaps the original Soho pleasure palace. She invited individuals from the great and good of the day to pay an annual subscription. For this they would receive a finely embossed card that allowed them entry to her grand, exquisitely decorated home, at any time, even in her absence. Her staff would be on hand to provide these chosen few with whatever was their hearts' desire, and at least once a week the lady of the house would throw a wonderful party. Even today, any *habitué* of the myriad spots around Soho would agree this format is very much still in use.

Whether or not it's something in the air or just the chemicals, Soho has always been a place for fun, frolics, picnics, parties and balls. Through the centuries, through the fashions, a leading society figure would always be holding some wondrous event attended by the A-listers of the day and their whores.

In the early twentieth century, flamboyant figures began to hold parties in various rather more discreet locations around Soho. One of these hosts devised a format based on a treasure hunt. He toured the streets handing out his invitations, upon which was written a series of clues. Those bright enough to figure out where and when the soirée was to be would surely make a party swing.

Soho continued to swing and swing some more; during the late fifties it became a centre for the burgeoning youth culture, and of course the sixties were crazy. After a brief lapse into misery in the seventies, when the austerity of the time did not sit too comfortably with the excesses synonymous with Soho, things began looking up again in the eighties.

London's lifelong addiction to hedonistic enterprise once again fought back. Soho was again the centre point. The Wag, the Pink Panther and Taboo were typical of the clubs and bars and venues where art-school kids and ageing artists mixed with club kids and ageing drag queens, with rich young kids and ageing socialites. Another character of Sohovian folklore, Phil Dirtbox, began his own version of the treasure-hunt parties, and they met with great success, culminating in his grand finale bash of 2000.

As we moved into the third millennium since our sky god's disciple was immortalised in our calendar, the continued gentrification of Soho and the resultant high cost of space conspired to rob Soho of many of the venues needed for these guerrilla dos, but Soho, unchanged in essence for some three hundred years, is still filled with the right kind of wrong people hunting for the same kind of fun and games. And just like it was in the good old days of the 1760s, there is always someone or something around to satisfy any need.

Yesterday, it was one of those sunny February days when the sun seems to stretch and strengthen its heat, thoughts of winter fade and the local *hoi polloi* flock to sit in Soho Square or Golden Square during breaks from their endeavours.

Vinnie here is a true Sohovian and always on his own little hunt for something or other. As he skips down Greek Street admiring the glimpses of his reflection in the windows, he stops and studies how his red patent shoes look with his new navy-blue pinstriped, made to measure by Meard Street's very own honorary Rolling Stone, John Pearce. While pondering whether the T-shirt he has on underneath it instead of something more formal makes him look like a hairdresser, he is interrupted by a shriek; he spins towards the sound – Vinnie lives for drama and commotion: his eyes alight upon Appolonia Greenblatt moving in.

Appolonia is the beloved daughter of a woman directly descended from Italian nobility and a Russian-Jewish wheeler-dealer of a father who made a mint in mining. Apples, as she is known to her friends, was a late and treasured gift, spoilt rotten and wanting for nothing. In spite of this, Appolonia is a charmer, a genuinely kind soul, incapable of causing offence despite her eccentric ways. Detached from reality, she floats thorough life on a cloud of rose petals, courtesy of Harvey Greenblatt.

'Darling, where are you off to?'

'Honey cherub, you're looking absolutely gorgeous as always,' Vinnie responds – although a native of the Walworth Road, he can schmooze with the best of them. He leans in to air kiss both of Apples' cheeks. 'I'm off to meet James at the Union. I think I introduced you to him at the club; he's one of my oldest friends. You may remember him – we make quite a sight turning up at parties, like Ratso and Joe Buck.'

Apples laughs even though she hasn't a clue who Ratso and Joe Buck are, let alone James. She must ask at lunch if the girls know them, where they all hang out?

'So, Appolonia, where are you off to on this gorgeous day?' Vinnie continues. Apart from his never-ending terms of endearment, he never could bring himself to call anyone by a nickname or abbreviation; call him old-fashioned, he won't mind.

'I'm going to the Ivy for a long Friday lunch with the girls. Abigail wants us to have a look at a flat at four before she makes a decision whether to buy or not – darling place, but not quite W1. She has been looking for an absolute age; none of us girls believes she will go through with this one either, so we have a plan. We're going to get her blotto at lunch and then make sure she puts in an offer, full asking price, on the spot. Tell me you don't think that's too mean, do you, Vinnie doll?'

'Wrong person to ask, my sweet, all is fair in love and war and indecisive friends as far as I'm concerned.'

They laugh and hug, promising to see each other later. A white van speeds past them, round the corner from Bateman Street, revving its engine and emitting a loud thumping bass. Appolonia steps back from the pavement edge and looks aghast. 'Oh Vinnie, I so need to get out of the city,' she says. 'Thank God some of the girls and I are getting down to the country tomorrow, to mummy and daddy's place – they're staying in town for the weekend to go to the theatre and some party. Winter has been so long and everyone is brassic; it's a cheap getaway. I can't wait to hear the birdsong in the morning – if I'm woken up by one more siren, I will scream. I simply can't take it any more.' Appolonia is twenty-two and heiress to a fortune; she even made it on to some hot heiress list on cable TV, so Vinnie knows that being broke means something entirely different to her.

One last mwah-mwah goodbye and Vinnie dashes past the little snail mosaic on the steps of the restaurant next door, and into the ruby-red entrance of the Union.

Appolonia continues down Greek Street and crosses over Cambridge Circus, nearly getting run over by yet another crazed white menace. What is it with this confluence of bedlam, Soho's very own spaghetti junction? This crossroads would be the perfect place for one of those maniacs who push people under tube trains to take their homicidal tendencies up to ground level; it's a real death trap. She negotiates the multiple crossings and dives down West Street to that wonderful oasis opposite the longest-running stage play in the world.

The darling doorman has known Appolonia since she was old enough to hold her own knife and fork and he welcomes one of his favourites to this glowing home from home. She feels her blood pressure stabilise as the coat check takes her Westwood duffel. She can almost taste the shepherd's pie already. Apples, unlike a number of her contemporaries, loves to eat.

Pulling open the surprisingly heavy door she enters the room. It has something of a tweedy, almost provincial décor, flooded with quite the rosiest glow you can imagine as the cool northern light is warmed by the kaleidoscope of golden and tawny leaded panes in the windows. The tablecloths are brilliant white and so, so crisp. The polished oak panelling is almost utilitarian in feel but glows with a loving burnish. Somehow it conjures up quite the most perfect English scene, very cosy – *Brief Encounter* in Technicolor.

After a couple of hours gossiping, drinking, eating and talking about how fabulous the Edgware Road is for late-night shopping, the girls head off to the Angel to view Abigail's latest option in the marathon that has been her property hunt. Perhaps situated a little too close to our last dear PM and his motley brood, it is, as Appolonia had pointed out to Vinnie earlier, definitely not quite W1.

Without any encouragement Abigail offers the asking price with a tipsy hiccup and they all stare in disbelief. The estate agent almost tap-dances out of the door. After agreeing to meet Flo and Scarlet later, Apples exits – *tout de suite*. Abigail heads off to mummy for housekeeping advice and a Valium. Flo and Scarlet head off to Soho, back to their favourite hunting ground.

It's now barely 8 p.m.; upstairs in the rickety doll's house that is this particular members' club overlooking Old Compton Street, we find these two, plainly in need of any kind of pick-me-up. Scarlet slams her ring-encrusted hand on the table with an annoying clunk and then taps her nails rhythmically to help her think. Her thoughts whirl. 'I'm in the middle of Soho,' she tells herself, 'there must be something around.'

'The thing is . . . ' Flo says, putting a firm hand on Scarlet's continuous tapping, silencing the aural torture. 'The thing is,' repeating herself, 'it's still early. All the dealers will be in bed or better still at last night's party, still thinking that it's last night.' Flo stares mournfully out of the window, and then slumps back into her worn leather wing-chair.

'I've got it!' screams Scarlet; then realising others can hear she whispers to Flo, 'Go and phone Vinnie, he will be at work by now and he'll know who's about. You call him, he's always loved you more than me.'

'That's only because you always flirt with Sonny,' snorts Flo.

'Come on, Flo, he will sort it out for you, you know he will. Let's get this gig on.'

Flo sighs, unwilling to be the one to make a move, but as she needs to spend a penny, she realises she can phone Vinnie while she's there. She finds a vacant cubicle in the ladies on the main landing, settles herself down, and scrolls through her phone to find Vinnie's work number. He shrieks with delight once she lets him know who is calling. Vinnie has always had a soft spot for Flo, among so many others.

'Florence how lovely to hear from you, how have you been? Now why have you not been around to see me, you naughty little minx.'

'Sorry, Vins honey, you know how it goes, work, work and then more work. Scarlet sends her love too.'

'How is that old tart anyway, she still after my DJ Sonny?'

'Oh Vinnie, that was a lifetime ago. And besides, you can't blame her, can you? Sonny is, as you always say, dynamic.'

Flo has the phone lodged between her head and shoulder; she manages to wipe herself dry, flush the loo and exit the booth while continuing this chatter; she has that art of multi-tasking while cradling the phone down to a T.

Vinnie grimaces when he realises what's going on at the other end of the phone. 'You could have phoned me when you had sorted your ablutions. Anyway, I suppose Scarlet is forgiven for now – she's on remand! So, honeysuckle, what can I do for you?'

'Well, since you so devilishly and cleverly ask, Scar and I are out on the hunt tonight for fun and frolics, meeting up later with Apples and probably Abigail, who will be in a complete state of shock about her new-found responsibility. You know me, in for a penny in for a pound, so we wanted to score something to help us cope with the scene. Can you help us get some bingo?'

'Florence, honey child, what kind of man would I be if I got you kids gak?'

'Oh please, Vins, if you can get us three Gs we'll split you half a gram.'

'Florence, you're such a temptress, and that little deal sounds like a good one to me. Let me think – mmmm, got it. Go and see if there's a black dominatrix type with big boots on, sipping coffee outside on Frith; if there is, you're in luck. Just sit down next to her and say that I sent you, tell her to phone me; whatever you do, make sure you don't ask her name.'

'Thanks, Vinnie, you're amazing! What should we do if she's not there? I mean what if she's whipping someone to within an inch of their life while telling them that they're a no-good cunt?'

Vinnie whooped; he loved to hear those posh girls swear like a navvy, great fun.

'Well, honey, if she's not there and she has got her groove on jigging a gig then we will go to plan B. But don't worry, we're still on plan A. Call me back if she's a no-show. Oh, Florence, you're so bad for me! You've got me really hungry for that marching powder; think I might go on a little manhunt for someone to share in my windfall. Don't worry, we'll get it sorted.'

'OK, Vins doll, when all is well and good, I'll stop by the desk and drop off your little present.'

As he hangs up, Vinnie smiles to the next waiting lost soul about to be pointed in the right direction. Meanwhile, Flo returns to Scarlet. As she passes one of the many small sash windows which dot the walls of this particular spot, she glances up at the only patch of visible sky: the moon has replaced the sun and the Devil has begun to dance.

While waiting for Flo to return, Scarlet too found herself looking out through the windows; she enjoyed the views from this members' eyrie, peeking into the rooms on the top floor of the theatre opposite. Were they some kind of obsolete entertaining space, she wondered. These rooftop vistas and glimpses of the sky really made this place, she thought. Most clubs in Soho were either dark or in basements; if there were windows they'd be blacked out with shutters or blinds. Perhaps the clientele would turn to dust if exposed to any sunlight. Scarlet giggled out loud at the thought, and knocked back another mojito, straightening up a little as she saw Flo return. After explaining the crazy caper that Vinnie had come up with, Flo dashed out the door, leaving Scarlet to return to her view of the Soho night.

Running down the stairs and out of Soho House, Flo bumps into two very handsome but poor-looking Spaniards who have been asking about jobs at the reception (those shoes of man-made materials are something of a giveaway). Juan and Fernando leave the club disappointed – no CV, no vacancies. They fall out of the door right into Harrison Avenue, the craziest agent in the whole of media land. Before the two can say a very broken 'sorry' – the only word that they know well is 'yes' – Harrison steams in. 'About time as well is all I can fucking well say. You'd better give a better blow job than the other cunts that your shit agency sent last time!' Frantically puffing on his cigar, he is about midway on his bender.

Juan and Fernando look at each other and then again at their new employer: the only word that they understood in the whole tirade was 'job'. They smile and nod as Harrison frogmarches them to the town-house hotel in Frith Street, room 21.

Back inside, Scarlet soon spots some guy, an editor type, sitting by the third sash over. Scarlet's eyes widen, her heart flutters a little, she prays that he is not too ripe.

The editor dude, sensing eyes upon him, turns in Scarlet's direction. She catches his glance, holds his stare for the requisite five seconds, then looks down at her empty glass. The gesture is understood, the game is on. He stands and walks towards the raven temptress. His shadow eclipses the table.

'Can I get your glass filled?'

Her eyes look up towards her latest deity. She takes to her stage, thinking how easy this performance is going to be. She languorously crosses her legs while subtly pulling up her skirt a few centimetres. Accepting the kind offer, she asks him to join her and have one as well, making up some random story about why her friend has bailed.

The drinks arrive, pleasantries are exchanged. Scarlet even uses her real name on this one. In no time at all, Mr Editor slides his wallet in Scar's direction.

'Would you like to powder your nose?'

She snatches the wallet while it's still in motion, and is off, slinking towards the powder room while smoothing her hands down over her hips and briefly across her Derby-winning arse. She knows he is watching her; he catches every nuance of her every move. His army begins to march, he is entrapped.

As Scarlet fixes her jet-black, almost navy-blue hair in the ladies, she laughs at the ease with which she can operate, enjoys this effect she has on men, has always had since she was fifteen. Then she checks her make-up to make sure that although she is the vixen her elder sister taught her to be she remains a kitten in her prey's estimation. She closes her eyes, beams.

Two mojitos and a few editing lines later, Scarlet leaves with the editor, back to his office on Beak Street for some more fun and games.

*   *   *

Meanwhile, back on Frith Street, Flo had sat down next to the only woman who could be a dominatrix; if she wasn't one, then this lady has just been to a fancy-dress party. Two headlights for eyes – adorned with electric-blue false eyelashes. Was she a woman or a drag queen?

Flo starts to smile as sweetly as she can.

'What do you want? And stop with the sugar, honey, just throw your dice.'

'Vinnie sent me.'

'How many?'

'Three.'

'OK can do. Only thing is, I've got this little number on; well, it's more of a full-length musical really. All singing, dancing and high kicks – my jazz hands are flexed for this puppy. If you want this now, you will have to stand in for me there till I get back.' Flo looks petrified. 'Don't worry, sister, he starts shouting first and that goes on for about a day and a half.'

The first time Cyn the dominatrix was sent to Harrison Avenue, he had answered the door looking as if a few thousand volts had been shot through him, shouting at some poor shrinking little waiter guy pinned against a wall in fear. Over his shoulder she had seen that reception dude, Vinnie, having a bath. 'Honeysuckle, why is this bath cold?' he had shouted at no one in particular. 'Elton would simply never put up with this.' Cyn had been sent to take over from Blair (a Dean Street hooker, who had left Soho in a hurry clutching a handful of cash and a bag of ice to her head). The reception dude had been amazingly unfazed by all going on around him, even when she disrobed and began playing her cunt like a harp. He just carried on fixing his hair in the mirror, talking shit about how late he was going to be by the time he got back to the desk. She had adored Vinnie ever since, and Harrison had pretty much paid her mortgage.

The dominatrix looks at Flo. 'Sweets, go to the town house in Frith Street, room 21. Don't worry, I will be there soon.' They leave in opposite directions. Just as Flo arrives at the entrance of the town-house hotel her phone rings: it's Vinnie singing down the phone. 'Listen, honeysuckle, I'll be waiting for you in room 22 so don't worry, we can take turns with Harrison. I've finished my shift; that lazy bitch Trudy, the skunk pussy, has taken over.'

Flo can't help but wonder if any of this is such a good idea; too late to back out now, she's already past the utterly uninterested receptionist and up the stairs. Flo is just about to knock when she hears the bellowing from inside. Very lightly she knocks on the door and it's wrenched open, almost dragged off its hinges by an insane-looking man who is naked except for his shoes and socks and is smoking his cigar despite the smoking ban. Flo cannot help but notice Harrison's shrivelled cocaine cock. Full of Head Girl bravado she walks slowly into the seedy scene, the room thick with the stench of testosterone. She instantly recognises the Spanish boys, how odd. They look slightly ashamed, the peseta has dropped and they are savvy to their role in this sordid scene. Flo, more than a little unnerved by the tableau before her, dashes into the bathroom to call Vinnie; relieved to hear his voice, she begins telling him all about the cute Spaniards. Vinnie, already in the next-door room, promises to be with her shortly to hold her hand, tells her just to go back into the bedroom and let Harrison scream for a while. 'He won't touch you, my sweet; honestly, I should know.'

Forty minutes later he is still shouting abuse. Flo has never heard anything like it. Although it was quite funny at the start, by this point she doesn't think she can take any more. She has been unable to get back on her phone and Vinnie has still not arrived. She is on the verge of running out when the door flies open.

The dominatrix screams into the room; seeing the look on Flo's face she pushes keys and a small package into her hand and tells her to scoot. The Spanish boys, now standing in their bikini briefs, are tossed another of the little packages – something to keep them interested. Flo does not wait; she's gone, leaning against the corridor wall outside to catch her breath. Looking down, she has in her hand the keys to room 22 and three grams of quality goods. Using the key while calling Scarlet, she enters 22. Scar is still with the editor; they arrange to meet up later. Inside she finds Vinnie lingering in the bath, reciting Spanish phrases while smoking a cigarette and exhaling into the extractor above him.

Out on the corner of Greek Street, two boys finally give up waiting for their punter to arrive, a little put out. They head off to the Box.

Inside Soho House, Apples and Abigail are drinking martinis with a twist.

'Oh, darling Apples, you do think that I've made the right decision, don't you?'

'Don't worry, you can always pull out and start again.' Apples downs her martini in one. 'Where is everyone . . . ?'

Carl Hopgood
Hand Shandy

Interview with a Rent Boy

'Hi there, how much would it be for an hour of your time?'

'Ninety in, a hundred and fifty out.'

'I'm sorry, could you explain that?'

'Ninety pounds if you come over to me – I'm just near Leicester Square – or a hundred and fifty if I travel to you in London. More if you want me somewhere else.'

'I don't want sex; I just want to talk to you. I'm not gay or anything.'

'No problem, buddy, whatever you want.'

Tragic, he thinks – just how many times has he heard that one?

'It's for research purposes only. I'm an actor. I'm supposed to be playing the role of a rent boy.'

'Sounds cool, mate, what do you want me to do for you?'

'I just want you to come over and talk. I'll ask you some questions, take some notes if you're OK with that.'

'Tell you what, for two fifty you can film the whole deal!'

'No, no, not necessary, I can just take notes. I can pay you a hundred and fifty pounds. I would really appreciate it.'

'What time are you thinking for this meet?'

'What's best for you? Any time.'

'Well, three till five in the afternoon is my quietest time. Between lunchtimes and end of work. After five gets busy in the week when guys finish at the office.'

'What about three tomorrow then?'

'Hang on.'

Daniel, the actor, waits while *Pete – twenty-five. Friendly English Lad. Hung, versatile and discreet*, checks his diary. It'd taken Daniel hours of reading all the papers that he'd found in that place on the corner of Rupert Street – that crazy gift shop, the one with all the lurid underwear – just to pick Pete. Searching through all the ads, he realised he had no idea how many guys there were out there flogging it, and just how buff they all looked. From what he could see in the photo, Pete was the closest in age, looks and offerings.

Is it such a good idea to take this role, he wonders. Maybe he is not all that comfortable with the idea? No, he reassures himself, it'll look cool, very hip and confident and the girls will love it.

'Yeah, that's fine. The number that's come up on my phone, can I use it?'

'Yes, of course.'

*   *   *

South London, three o'clock the following afternoon. Pete (in reality Christopher, almost twenty-eight and from Peterborough) presses the intercom at the scruffy entrance to an old semi-industrial building a few minutes from Vauxhall Bridge. This was a handy little earner, he thought, nice and near to his flat.

What's more, as Pete has yet to get off today, if this is legit and he still feel horny afterwards, he's just around the corner from Vauxhall's gay village.

Before he can announce himself, the door buzzes and vibrates in response. Inside, a long dark corridor leads to the foot of the staircase. He hears a voice: 'All the way up.'

At the top stands Daniel (Andrew, almost thirty-one, from Derby). He stretches out to greet Pete who shakes his hand rather formally. Daniel is struck by how firm Pete's grip is, how full his bicep looks in the sleeve of his jerkin. He picked well; this guy appears pretty regular, fit and strong. Just the type of guy Daniel wants to portray. This movie rent boy is to be no tragic character, just a shrewd young businessman. Daniel can sniff the good reviews already. Well, he could if his nostrils were not still blocked from last night. They introduce themselves to each other, Daniel prefers Dan, Pete prefers Pete.

Inside, the industrial space of Daniel's flat has been transformed into a rather cool pad, although it is extraordinarily messy. The young Brazilian woman who had been cleaning it just hadn't appeared for weeks. Perhaps she was on to a more lucrative position – she had the body.

Pete accepts Daniel's offer of a beer, and sits between some of the discarded jackets and other clothing left strewn over the sectional sofa that dissects the space. Daniel manages to find a few left in the fridge among the takeaway cartons that have started to smell a little.

He pours himself a slug of Ketel One, knocks it back, then takes the Budvar back to Pete, who looks somehow more approachable now. Daniel relaxes a little, the Ketel One helping – this is all fine. Everyone's cool.

He sits on his Eames recliner opposite Pete, and lights up a Marlboro Red. Pete takes one when it's offered.

Daniel leans back. 'You might recognise me, probably wondering where you've seen me.' Without waiting for an answer he continues. He tells Pete of his starring role in the latest gritty cult TV series. Daniel had been slogging away on the fringe-theatre scene and in the voiceover studios in Lexington Street. Just another of those soap-dodging young actors trying to be the next big thing. Finally last year he got the lead in a new series, which turned out to be a bit of a success, all the cast believing that they, and not their characters, were now household names.

Pete doesn't say anything during this, more than anything he is just relieved that this guy is more Jude Law than Ricky Gervais. He scans Daniel's loft: it's a bit messy, but he likes the space and wishes his own place in Charing Cross Road had as much character. He is not sure if he recognises Daniel or not; he's kind of familiar, but then he has that look.

'Is it still all right for me to take notes?' Daniel asks. 'I'm going to be playing a male escort in a new Brit flick. It could be great for me, it's my first big film role. I tell you what, I'll get you a ticket for the première.'

'Sure, sounds great,' Pete says, still not entirely sure if all of this is for real. 'How do you want to do this? What do you want to ask? Go ahead, whatever you want to know.'

'Let me grab my laptop. I made some notes, thought of some questions.' Retrieving his computer, he takes a deep breath as if entering stage left. 'This is a bit of a weird scene, best I just get straight to it. Apologies if I offend, no offence meant. Feel free to veto any questions, OK? Let's start off easy. How long have you been a male escort?'

Pete begins to think, tries to remember which year of uni it was that he first got some money out of it. Reminds himself again that he markets himself as twenty-five.

'Around three years, I guess. A guy I met in London one summer before I moved here must have thought I looked like rent and left me fifty quid in the morning. Seemed like easy money, so I went back to Leeds where I was at uni, got some pics and put an ad in the local gay rag. Simple as that.'

'University, really? What was your degree?'

'English; got a 2:2, might have been better if I wasn't working so much the last year,' Pete laughs.

'Really, that's interesting, I can use that. So you started in Leeds. How long have you been in London?'

'Two years now, I had a proper job when I first arrived. But I was out of there within six months and even while I was working I was still making extra money with this.'

'So how many more years do you have left escorting?'

'Well I can't say I escort much if you know what I mean, just an hour or two at mine or theirs, job's done. Hope to leave them happy, then there might be some repeat business. Seriously pal, in answer to your question, it's a young man's game, gets a little tragic much beyond thirty, unless you're gonna become some serious dungeon master! As soon as I've finished my master's I'm done with this gig. Hopefully I will pass it this year, my second resit. Too many late nights, too many early mornings. Listen, it's been pretty good doing this to get through. I can work more or less when I want. Got a decent flat in Charing Cross Road, a Mini Cooper S.'

'So you have regular clients then?'

'Yeah, I have a few guys. Generally from out of town, married, come to London on biz every few months. Don't want to bother with going out, just want to get off. I've had a couple of guys fly me out to wherever. One time, I got taken out to Edmonton for a rodeo, the guy had a farm in Alberta as big as fucking Wales. Of course I met him here, but he flew me out there a few times. Now those jobs pay seriously well.'

'So are most of your clients – is that the right term? – married?'

'To be honest, I'm not really that sure. I know that a few of them are, especially the ones that like to talk. And I'm pretty sure most of them probably do lead straight lives, divorced or whatever. But a lot identify as gay. Older ones who don't get any play otherwise. Mainly though it's regular gay guys who just want to fuck and can't be bothered to go out. Too busy, too tired. They can see what I've got to offer, they want some of it, it's a buyer's market. Client, punter, john, if they're pretending to live out some porno fantasy, they're all the same.'

'So what do you identify yourself as?'

'I'm just your average gay lad with a bigger than average dick, having some fun and getting paid for it.' Again Pete laughs. 'Listen mate, I'm twenty-five, big cock and always horny, so why not?'

He has a handsome face, smallish features, cute. A bright lad, from a forgettable part of England. He'd used his not inconsiderable charms to pretty good effect. From a regular family, who still got on surprisingly well. His father had been a little difficult when he discovered his first and only son to be gay. There'd been some ugly scenes, a little violence, but it's hard to express yourself when you're a tough site manager for a provincial construction company.

'So have you ever experienced any violence during your work?'

Strange, Pete thought, that he should ask him that just as he was thinking of his father.

'No, Dan, not during work time. You have to be able to look after yourself in this game. I get to the gym most days, do my boxing, and me and my mates, we look after each other. I have a buddy who does this as well; we make a pretty good duo for those that want that. He'll be phoning me when our hour is up, just to make sure everything's cool. It's not like being some whore on Old Compton. We don't need minders and we especially don't need pimps.'

Most of the lads in this game are pretty clean; only get on it at the weekend. Pete smiles broadly; they do look after each other and certainly the guys he knows in the business are clean, partying is left for weekends. Apart from the Viagra, which even Pete uses on occasion and considers should be tax-deductible, and the odd spliff, anything harder is purely for recreation.

'We're not a bunch of junkies, trying to get enough together for our next bump. We don't often have to deal with clients bigger and stronger than ourselves. It's much more difficult if you're a bird doing this.'

'So you work out every day then?'

'Got to, doing this. I turn up – you must want to get it on, pay me for my time, you know?'

Daniel does know, his game is not so different. Always being judged on his appearance. Always trying to be whatever the casting director or whoever wants him to be. It really is not so different at all.

'It's you straight guys I feel sorry for – when you get horned up in the West End on a Friday night, look at the options you have. At least if you're gay you can just pick up a paper and dial up whatever floats your boat. We've created a pretty nifty little world for ourselves, us gay boys. It's not like taking your chances in some dodgy brass house. You have a look next time; they're lined up on the stairs. And you know what, some of those lads are not too shabby. Would be happy to do them myself.'

'So I guess you've got to be well hung then to do this job?'

'Ha ha, it helps. I'm sure if you've got a great ass and only get fucked it's not so important, although you're already limiting your market. But you know, most gay men are size queens. Even on a bottom it's good to have a meaty cock to play with.'

'I guess I can understand that, I like playing with my own dick!' Daniel felt his face warm a little as he said that and wasn't sure why he did. Pete, not at all embarrassed, was wondering the same. 'This is great, just the kind of stuff I wanted. It will really help me with my role.'

'So what role do you prefer then, mate?' Pete grins.

He's getting into this, can't quite figure out this Daniel. Pete keeps wondering if he's getting the vibe.

'Usually doggy with a bitch,' Daniel shoots back, his embarrassment obviously over.

There is definitely something going on here, thinks Pete, and the idea of Daniel fucking like a dog is getting him a little horny. Maybe he will have to hit the nearby sauna when he's finished, catch a few guys leaving work early. That's always a good show. Can usually have quite a few in a couple of hours on their way back to the missus. Pete's getting a chubby at the thought.

Daniel is watching Pete; he is being drawn into this, this guy, this situation. And he is OK with it – isn't he? It's not so strange after all. This young man selling himself for sex is perhaps just a slightly different, slightly younger version of himself. It's easy talking like this with him, easier than talking to a woman about sex would ever be. Upfront and straightforward. Daniel sees the appeal. His mind wanders; is it really good to have a big cock to play with while you're fucking? He finds himself wondering what Pete's cock would taste like.

Without thinking, Daniel adjusts his hardening cock.

Tracey Emin – Number One Door Whore

No. 1 Door Whore

It was like being inside of a giant kettledrum. The noise of the pelting rain on the caravan roof was deafening. At least the outskirts of High Wycombe was not the tropics, so really heavy rain only fell occasionally.

Cassie reached for the Buddha pot she had bought in Thailand when King was still a baby. Seamus had paid for them to go away while the club was getting its licence back – she had thought that maybe King should become a Buddhist.

She yanks off Buddha's head and pulls out her last strip of Valium. The weed just isn't mellowing her out enough.

'King, roll us another joint, babes. How long is it going to keep raining?'

King begins to skin up. 'It's not so bad, Cass, it's quite rhythmic,' he grins.

'I guess – tribal man!' She pops a blister and swallows her little blue friend hungrily.

'Can I cut this for a roach?' King asks.

'No, not that, that's my invite. Seamus is having his fiftieth, everyone's going to be there . . . we're going to this one; I'm planning to network like crazy. Maybe he'll put me back up the front of one of his new places. Just think about it, King! We could move back to London, how crazy that would be? We'd do it properly this time. You could work for me doing the music, just like a proper family business.'

'Sounds great, mum. Let me know when the bus leaves.'

'*Cass*, not mum, you only call me that to wind me up. Why are you always so down on my ideas? You think I'm past all that but I'm not – we are really going to go this time; those people remember me, every fucker in town knew me then. If I was on their door the whole of London would turn up. Even the W11 crowd. That lot always had the best drugs and the best parties, don't care what anyone says about them, assholes or not. You could lose days and the drugs were still flowing; boy were they strong! – not like that cut-up shit in Soho. I remember one party, there was so much gak that even after two days it was piled high in the basin. I had to get rid of one creep by tossing a plate of it out the door like a frisbee; you should have seen him run.

'Poor little King, though, your namesake. King the First. I get choked up thinking about him. I never even realised he was missing till the next day. Elroy, your shitty no-good father, I never forgave him really. Fancy shoving MDMA up his little ass. It was the beginning of the end, two years later we were finished.

'What a way to go though, just like the little rock star he was – passed out and choked on his own vomit. Tell you what, not many chihuahuas are as famous as he was. You had to be nice to my dog or you weren't getting in anywhere.'

Cass claps her hands, 'Enough of that . . . So, lover boy, whadaya think? Not bad, eh? This bird is holding up well, ain't she?'

She stands in front of the full-length mirror attached to the back of the door that separates off her sleeping area. She undoes the shapeless old robe she seems to live in these days. Underneath she has on some old La Perla's. The lace edges have long since given up the ghost and the darned areas stand out black on the greyed satin, she pushes up her tits and sucks in her gut. The ripples and dimples are obvious, but if she squints and smoothes she can recapture the feeling. Imagine once again how it felt to be fit and desired. She was a bit of a hottie in her time, and was never slow when it came to feeding her snatch, as she would say.

King found himself staring as her hands smoothed the line of her panties.

He was noticing the fullness and slight creasing. Cass spoke and he suddenly remembered who this was, his mother. He took a last look, a toke on the joint and then passed it to her, give her something else to do.

She sucked hungrily on the soggy end, and then flicked it in the sink. 'So, honey, what should I do with the hair? They'll expect it. I never had the same do twice. Sometimes it was even a don't.' She laughs, hollow but loud. She lifts up her hair, checking the roots, trying to remember what colour she really was. Mouse with grey highlights, she decides, always a winner.

Then the unmistakable strains of that theme tune interrupt. King starts searching for the remote. The Panasonic 40-inch dominates the corner of the living area – bought when the latest thing, but within months made obsolete by the flat screen.

Tara's rather manic face appears with a giant outdoor microphone to fill the screen.

'Good-evening, here we are once more . . .'

Not that old slag again. But, by God, she fell on her feet.

Cass starts down the same track she always gets on when seeing Tara's face. One day many years before they had competed to see who was the biggest door whore of all. Cass had wiped the floor with her at that gig, but now Tara was huge and not just because of the pregnancy. Married to a Shakesperian actor, she was breeding merrily while still presenting prime-time TV.

'We we're all pissing ourselves that night when the crabs were scuttling between her eyebrows. Me especially because I put them there – indirectly, of course, never really got into the mattress munching.

'I had been seeing Pascal for a while, at least for the lift home to Deptford. Even after he gave me a dose that took two rounds of penicillin to shift, I kept him happy for that lift, never even told him. My revenge was setting Tara up with him knowing he'd spread it around. Worked better than I could have ever imagined. He'd caught crabs in the meantime and sure enough the day after blowing him in the car, she was standing at that opening with those bushy eyebrows alive with those little suckers. Someone screamed while talking to her but she still didn't get it. Later that night she was seen rushing from the toilets straight out the door, legging it down Beak Street. No one saw her for days and when they did she still had that scent of eau-de-kill-crab.

'She was a dirty bitch that one, but fun nevertheless. One night when we were out having cocktails – what was that place called? It was on Kingly . . .' Cass's mind wanders momentarily. 'Anyway, you know what she asked the poor fucking waiter?'

'Cass . . .' King has heard all this before – often.

Cass is already laughing and snorting, and can barely finish the story. ' "Put your tray down and get your cock out; let's see how far you can pull it back." And you know what? He did and she noshed it there and then. Dirty cunt.'

'Cass, too much info.'

'You are a little priss, aren't you? But so smart. You are going to be the first in the family to go to uni; I know it. You've already managed one more year than I did at school, two more and you can go to college. Make a fortune and keep your mum in style in her old age.'

Cass reaches for another of her little blue helpers. She takes two this time.

Stocks are getting low; how is she going to get back to Goa to stock up?

She knows she won't. She is just going to have to make it up with Jamie; Lord knows, those trolley dollies get the best quality Valium.

Cass is aware that this chance could well be her last to get back in the loop. She needs to go and make it work. It will be tough, but she really needs this.

The parties, the openings, the hair and the heels. The men. She really needs a good seeing to. She is hungry too for the power. That thrill she used to get when telling those sad fucks that their names ain't on the list – you ain't getting in – 'bye!

King is bored by yet another trip down memory lane. He rummages around in the bin beneath the seat cushions; he finds the canvas wrap and pulls it out.

'Oh, King, do you really need to?'

'Yeah, mum, you will have some as well.'

'OK, but only to be with you, baby.'

He unties the package revealing his works: spoon, baggy and syringe. The needle is still good for a few more goes. He gets to work intently.

Cass is beginning to drift finally; the diazepam and the weed at last seem to kick in.

She will go to Seamus's birthday. It will be great, she will look fantastic and they will love her all over again. This time she will do it right, make it work.

'Here, Cass, you first. I've got it ready, where do you want it?' She gives him her hand, fingers parted wide.

As the narcotic enters her body, her demons as well as the rain are temporarily silenced. Calm reigns. Cass leans back on the banquette, soon enough King joins her. She smiles at him, the man of the house. Well, the mobile home . . .

Jonathan Yeo – Autumn Leaves

The Seduction of a Straight Man

In spite of the grey surroundings there are vivid splashes of colour in Soho. Particularly at night, the lights and people combine into quite a spectacle for the uninitiated. But perhaps the most colourful aspects of all are the experiences and misadventures that people tend to share in its many corners.

Take this group of friends, out in one of the many Soho watering holes one night: Carol had been settled in London for many years (Toronto wasn't hard to leave behind), a Canadian agony aunt whose advice was best not taken. Notorious for the state of her own intimate relationships, she was in dire need of some sound advice herself. Despite this, the one thing she wasn't was stupid. She was the first to realise she needed to take stock, she knew that in spite of her frequent trips to Madame Verushka's beauty parlour, there was another kind of depilation that desperately called for attention. It was her men that Carol needed to shave: she had a habit of growing one beard of a husband after another and ultimately they always had to be shaved off. Although she chuckled to herself at her analogy, the sad truth was that a beard on a woman in her forties was not the best of features and a definite hindrance to future satisfaction.

Carol was with her tight coterie of gal pals that evening, she needed the camaraderie of their shared hormones, needed some validation – her job having given her the vocabulary at least of a therapist. Between gulps of Canadian Club she talked through her demons without ever being specific, another trick gleaned from writing her column.

The four of them were gathered to the side of a large roaring fire, quite one of the most soothing to be found in these parts. On this stormy, rainy evening you could almost imagine snowy Alps outside the window when ensconced in this particular spot, not some Hellenic streetscape. Greek Street, one of Soho's cross streets, was a combination of everyday businesses and party places wrapped up in not the most glamorous of clothes. It had an air of being on the edge and almost out of the loop, but this was all part of its gritty charm.

Above the fire was a mournful, staring moose head – no, it's not the Alps we're in, it must be the Adirondacks. Dotted through this room, which was a lunch spot during the day and only became a drinking spot at night, was a collection of totally mismatched fixtures and fittings. With a special emphasis on funky lights, it was a prime example of the interior-decoration style known as 'my old student dorm on acid'. You will have seen this style before – sofas like the one your aunty had in the seventies on her shag-pile rug, knick-knacks handed down by granny, Blue Lady pictures and all. All this stuff was mixed in with some battered twentieth-century pieces. It was unpretentious and much more low-key than the other members' clubs. That was all part of its charm. The carpet might be a little threadbare, but if you were not in the mood for show, it was the perfect warm and secluded spot.

James, another Soho *habitué*, turned up outside. He was feeling a little low-key himself that night. He prided himself on his slightly unusual take on the world and felt comfortable on the fringes as long as they were the fringes of the main event. The Union suited him well. He rang the bell and waited . . . he rang the bell again and waited a little longer; as he leaned into his third ring the heavy front door flew out towards him, but he was prepared for this and jumped back with ease, preventing a bloody nose.

Carol spotted James as soon as he came in. They were old friends, and although wimminhood was great for a while, as far as Carol was concerned, there was nothing like a bit of testosterone to liven things up. James was the one guy she knew with whom she felt comfortable chewing the fat. Although men were all wankers and worms, snivelling little boys who never grew up – or so she thought that night – James's charms were irresistible and it didn't hurt that he was also rather dreamy.

He joins the sorority; his date is late, very late, always busy at work and always with another message to send. It's best that James doesn't think too much about all that, because in spite of his rather hard exterior, underneath it all James is just another slightly bruised softie; he is certainly no angel, but his heart is true and he always hopes for the same loyalty in return. There are nights when he too thinks all men are jerks, but being a man himself, and sometimes even a jerk, he knows all too well the inherent weaknesses of the gender and is very forgiving.

Carol continues to skirt vehemently around the real issue. The other gals and James listen intently. They are all very fond of Carol, she is great fun and with her raspy voice, tweaked with the whisky and a few too many sneaky cigarettes, she is always good to listen to.

If there is one insight she's had in all those years of dishing out stupid advice it is that relationships are always some kind of charade. She is evangelical about this, or is that older and wiser? Of course, she couldn't quite admit her own charade, but as is the way with most journalists she has a big enough ego to put the world to rights.

James too knows all about this masquerade. He too has a need to enlighten; Venus and Mars are still too close.

He tells the gang that all men like to fuck, and not just their wives or partners, and it's time that women got hip to that. Men including him are basically weak; when the dick is hard anything in its way will be fucked. Despunking is really as everyday as a crap. Gay, straight or, like most, some combo of the two, Alfred Kinsey was right all along.

Homosexuality has for many years been something of a Soho speciality. There are those who seek it out to gawk at it, then go running back to those comfy suburbs that contain many happy gay folk getting on more quietly with their lives, in most ways no different from anyone else in Acacia Avenue. Soho, on the other hand, attracts the party boys, the prowlers, the horny and the horned, as well as the occasional visit by those nervous off-the-train-for-the-night types. It is an especially hot spot for two particular animals. The 'straight' guy from somewhere else who wants to suck cock, and the gay guy from anywhere who is only too pleased to oblige, in fact you could say it's his calling.

James continues to educate the uneducated. He illustrates his lesson with a couple of tales from an old sparring partner, notorious around these parts. The girls are transfixed.

The seduction of a straight man by a gay man is to its practitioners something of an art form, and it is not, as the old joke says, a question of 'just one more pint'.

No, the seduction of a straight man by a gay man is rather more complicated than that, but definitely not as challenging as some other art forms, and usually done solo and in silence. It is all to do with timing, as so many things in life are. Get the timing right and bingo! Some would say it's evil, some would say it's sexy, and others would say it's a dammed good experience.

You find yourself in a crowded bar, the guy that you want in your way tonight is out of the way of his missus for the evening. You are trying to get a fix on the vibe. Glances are being exchanged, men of all sexual persuasions are constantly checking other men out – don't believe otherwise. But the signs he's giving out are confusing: changing from go, to back off, to go again; well, you can always try this trump card as a final ball breaker – or is that ball catcher?

Simply walk over to the chosen one and confidently murmur into his ear about how the three women you have slept with have not turned you straight, so why should him having sex with you turn him gay?

That little piece of information has worked so many times for the experts it's quite frightening to think how easy guys really are.

The next words of wisdom James shares are altogether more about right place, right time.

Now picture this scene. You find yourself working in a little town-house hotel in Soho; you're on the closing shift but also you're on a back-to-back. For those not in the know, those are the shifts when you close for the night and then open up the next day, it can be a real drag. This night you're lucky enough not to have sold all the rooms so there is one left for you. On your way to bed you find on the staircase a figure that you recognise. A face that you remember seeing many times on those Soho streets. But all you have ever done is nod to each other.

'Hi,' you say.

'Oh hi,' he replies.

'Are you OK?' you ask.

'Not really,' he admits. 'I've just had a row with my girlfriend and she's banished me for the night.'

You sit and turn on the sympathy. Oh, how awful, you tell the poor guy, who is, as it turns out, quite devilishly handsome in an ageing rockabilly kind of way. You two have never been properly introduced, and as the poor bedless guy's hair falls seductively over his eyes, you show a little interest in the stud's predicament. That's all it really takes, a compassionate ear – or so it would seem.

He tells his story. He and his old schoolfriend plus respective girlfriends had been out all night eating, drinking, merrymaking. At some point one of their peckers had got hard and the conversation had turned to thoughts of their two gals kissing. An oldie, but a goodie. The girls had been happy to oblige, but insisted that they would do so only after the guys had kissed first. This had been immediately dismissed as not going to happen, as it so often is on first hearing. But on a subsequent trip to the toilet stall to top up their energy reserves, our rockabilly guy and friend talked themselves into kissing for the bitches. In fact, so energised were they, they decided not only to kiss but also really to get into it with each other. It would get the girls totally horned up. After all, it wouldn't mean anything – they had known each other for twenty years.

After performing for the girls in the deserted residents' library upstairs, they found the reaction was not quite what they'd envisaged. His girlfriend turned out not to be so cool and went ballistic when she saw her boyfriend's tongue down another guy's throat. No, it was not a turn on; she had freaked, told him to not come back that night and that she would be in touch . . . The girls had stormed out, leaving the poor hapless guys behind. Rocker's buddy had run after them, but his own girl was feistier and he knew it was wiser to back off.

The trouble was, he found himself without anywhere to go. His keys and everything else he really needed were back at her place, so he had stumbled down the stairs, and finding himself on a quiet landing with an inviting wing-chair, he had slumped into it hoping just to sleep for a while.

But of course he can't stay there; the night porter is a jobsworth and checks all the corridors throughout his shift. But you know the room down the corridor is empty – it's the one you cheekily kept back for yourself.

A little smile comes over you. You tell the guy that he will only be thrown out in the rain if he stays there, so he should come with you; he will be OK, just this way . . . the man follows silently, you enter room 21 and close the door behind you both – job done.

And then in the morning you still don't know each other's name, and when next you pass each other on the street all you will do is nod.

Carol has listened throughout. She knows a version of this story only too well.

She tells them all that husband number three is going to get well and truly shafted by her, because he never shafted her in close to five years.

Don't they know that's just what straight men want? James roars.

Sam Taylor-Wood
The Ballerina

The Ballerina

One evening the other week, Jeanne, a slightly-passed-her-prime ballerina with something of a co-dependent, addictive personality and an international reputation, came pirouetting through the foyer.

An hour earlier she had touched down at Heathrow on her way back from the US. She was heading home to her North London hillside, but had needed to stop off at the bar *en route*. She was well past eight months pregnant and only the Americans would ever have put her on a plane, terrified no doubt that she might drop on their soil.

'Hi, Vinnie darling, how are you? My taxi is waiting, so I'm just going to grab my case. I know where it is.' Without waiting for an answer, and with her usual lopsided, wide-eyed, chemically assisted grin, she disappeared into the cloakroom.

At Vinnie's side was Trudy, her calls constantly on hold, chatting mindlessly but always flirtatiously with some potential little earner.

When Jeanne emerged triumphant with a wheelie-bag, Vinnie immediately spotted that there was a potential fly in the ointment.

'Are you sure that's your bag, Jeanne?' he shouted out, mid-sentence of his phone conversation.

'Yes, darling, of course! Oh, you're so cute when you're rattled, Vinnie!'

Vinnie quickly tied up his phone call, knowing this needed further investigation.

'I'm sure that is someone else's bag,' he said to Trudy, as Jeanne hurried off.

'Don't worry about it, Vinnie baby, it ain't our bag,' Trudy replied, without breaking the steely eye contact she had locked on to her next intended score.

As all of this has been happening, Connery O'Brien has been sitting in the restaurant entertaining clients. Despite the fact that he is generally regarded as one of the slimiest producers in the film business, he has always had a special place in Vinnie's heart; there is something about that big nose and his rampant heterosexuality that he finds appealing.

'Listen, dude, you don't get my angle. I tell you what, you should just send your bitch of a secretary around, she gets my angle just right,' he says, rising from his chair and, as usual, leaving his clients to settle the bill. As he enters the bar, he sees that ballerina he used to nail spin out of the doors at the far end. Vinnie looks on anxiously as the coked-up, very pregnant ballerina/choreographer/good-time gal heads out the main door with bag unknown.

*   *   *

'Vinnie, can you deal, someone wants to book a room and I can't remember the name of the place we use when the others are full.' It's Trudy's dulcet tones bringing Vinnie back to the present time. He grabs the phone she has outstretched towards him.

'Please tell me you can get a room tonight in that naughty little hotel of yours. I've been banished from L'air du Temps; can't tell you why, not now, I will fill you in later; tell me you can get a room – cheap?' the caller pleads. No introduction was necessary for Vinnie; he knew Molly Hugh's voice too well. Newspaper columnist and recently sacked film critic on daytime TV, her voice betrayed her formative years singing in the valleys.

'Yes, yes, I can get a room, just come round. What time are you going to be here?'

'I'm just round the corner in a taxi. I've not got any cash on me at the minute. Do you think I can blow him for the fare?'

'Better make sure he's not one you've done before. If he says no, tell him I'll give him one this end.' He hangs up.

Molly roars with laughter, relieved she has a bed for the night, back on home turf. She is glad to be out of that suffocating place on the Loire, where she was treated as the rich foreigner everyone could rip off.

The final straw had come just two days earlier, when she was physically chased down the twisting medieval streets by a pack of locals, rather like that scene from *Suddenly Last Summer*. All this, just for walking across the fields and through town singing to herself. The fact it was at first light, she was blind drunk and dressed like a nun with no knickers and the urge to lift up her habit to prove it, seemed immaterial to Molly. When the local Monsignor on his way to church saw her singing 'I Have Confidence In Me', he ran into the *pâtisserie* and set the mob on her.

Her taxi rattled to a halt outside Helpdesk Soho.

So here we are, a scene from where our story is set. Helpdesk Soho, the lobby of an otherwise unimportant location. It formed the beating heart of the local scene and was manned by Vinnie Valentine and his cohorts. There was Trudy Tryhard, 'the laziest bitch on earth', as Vinnie described her, 'the archetypal last born'. Trudy won't do anything for anyone unless there is a lot in it for her. Her boyfriends are always minted and usually buddies of each other. They last barely a month each. At the start it's always sweetness and light, she shows them a good time, but within a month it's summonses at dawn.

*   *   *

Lauren enters the fray; a part-timer on the desk, she is relieving Trudy who at twenty-four wants a tit tuck and is having a last-minute dinner date with a noted plastic surgeon. Lauren works days at Mystic FM – an MOR radio station. Famous for her voice, which evokes velvet rubbed the wrong way, and with her ample breasts and a startling resemblance to the bride of Chucky, she brings a touch of *The Rocky Horror Show* to our setting. Personally, Vinnie can't wait to see the back of Trudy and have Lauren the trouper on board. Who knows, she might even tackle some of Trudy's backlog.

As usual Molly Hugh's entrance cannot be missed. Barely four feet ten inches tall, she is wearing her favoured outfit, an ill-fitting Japanese designer costume. There are matching boots as well, just made for walking and pinching her chubby ankles.

'Thank God for this place,' she begins to bellow as soon as the door cracks open. She loves an entrance, is almost high kicking her way up to the desk.

'Vinnie sweetheart, you're an angel, where would we be without you? I'll slip you some cash tomorrow when I've been to the bank. Do me a favour, darling, and get me my favourite French waiter to help with my luggage. I still think those Frenchmen are hot in spite of themselves and that one especially needs to be taught a lesson or two.' She winks at Vinnie while absent-mindedly fondling her breast. Vinnie, feeling a little nauseous at the sight, needs to get rid of this one sharpish.

'Here you go, Molls darling, here's your reservation number, and the hotel is expecting you. I'll send Pascal round with your bag in the next half hour – give you time for that extra scrub,' he winks back hard, to end this episode.

She leaves, still fondling. Trudy slopes off next, off to dinner. Without waiting for Lauren to arrive and take over, she has miraculously managed to put on a whole new face, with some higher heels, all while Molly was centre stage. Handily, Lauren arrives moments after and grabs the nearest ringing phone.

Meanwhile, throughout all this, Jeff Perry, movie mogul, has been standing by patiently, waiting to grab Vinnie's attention; he is expecting a very important package to be sent to the desk for him. Staying in the neighbourhood, like everyone else it seems, he relies on this place to act as a concierge service during his visit. He is getting a little frazzled.

'Darling Jeff, just look at you standing there, the strong and silent type – my favourite. All American pie and handsome. You'd better watch out, my stalker genie will escape from its bottle. I'm all yours.'

'Vinnie, there's an irate gibbering wretch on the phone – something about a suitcase?'

'Jeff darling, I'll be with you in a sec.' Vinnie grabs the phone, speaks quickly to Jeanne, her anxiety rising. He writes down a number, gets rid of her and turns and flicks his beloved locks in his best shampoo-ad style, forgetting his concerns for a moment and flashing a newly polished grin.

Finally Jeff gets his moment in Vinnie's spotlight.

Jeff, disarmed by the sheer weight of Vinnie's rather deep and meaningless charms, is just relieved to be speaking at last.

'Remember I am expecting a really important parcel. As soon as it arrives I have to know – you have my cell and hotel-room numbers, don't you?'

'As soon as, my sweetness. I have all your details; your room is next to this crazy broad I know – so I can't forget!'

'I'm off for a meeting. Is there anywhere with a terrace where we can smoke?' Jeff asks, needing his cigar badly.

'Nowhere good. The Twentieth has four walls around its roof terrace so smokers aren't allowed until the appeal. The Doll's House has a terrace so small they can only let seven on at a time – standing room only. Next door don't even have any outdoor space so you're on the pavement if you want a fag. The only place I can think of is the Green Hole, where they still think its 1983 – I doubt if they even know about the ban. But that's like walking into the pub on the moors in *An American Werewolf in London*; the owner looks like he's already in purgatory.'

'Why the hell is no one setting up terraces over here?'

Vinnie shrugs. 'It's the council, they're not allowing anyone to build terraces. They want everyone to give up, but failing that they are terrified this lot would end up falling from the roof. Natural selection if you ask me.'

Jeff leaves for his meeting, looking like a man with concerns.

Vinnie reaches for the phone, dials that pregnant ballerina's number and waits.

A loud booming voice abruptly fills the short-lived silence. 'I'm off for a meeting. I will be back in a few for my suitcase.' It's Connery O'Brien, gone out the door before anyone can answer.

Vinnie slams the phone down; in a flash he knows this is the answer to strung-out Jeanne's lost luggage. He goes into the cloakroom, his very own den of ill repute. It is the usual mess in there. He picks his way through the assorted bags and coats strewn around and finally, there in the corner, he sees, oh my God, a Samsonite. That stupid trollop has picked up Connery's Tumi and left her cheap one here.

Lauren, meanwhile, left alone at the desk, has been directing the courier guy with the urgent package in the direction of the small town-house hotel around the corner.

Vinnie returns to his seat behind the desk and gets to work sorting out the suitcase fiasco.

When he is finished he turns to Lauren. 'Thank God that's sorted. She wants whatever is in her bag back there *tout de suite* . . . I'm tempted to take some *suite* for myself. She is sending over a cab with Connery's in it and it's been told to take hers back. That cheap bitch wanted us to cover the cost, so I told her if she wants it she pays – no dice, baby.'

'Great Vinnie, you're a sensation. By the way, daddyo, the package came for Jeff. I remembered he wanted to remain anonymous so I just put room 101 on it and sent it round.'

'For the love of God, that's the room they put Frances de la Mare in. When she checked in yesterday they put her in 22, and she kicked up such a fuss about the generator noise, they gave her 21 and put Jeff in 22 a few hours later. Did you not see the note from Trudy?'

Lauren looks confused.

'You know Frances de la Mare, that old crow, has just had a full body tuck and is in room 21 – not to be disturbed at any cost for at least forty-eight hours; she can barely move and has her own drip in there.' Frances, an ageing actress determined to stay forever young, has the temper of an unpaid whore.

'There was no note. Trudy left nothing except a full inbox.'

'That useless gold digger is such a waste of space – she'd better quit before she's pushed, that one. Hold the fort, Lauren, I have to run.'

He dashes through the door, his little legs pumping. He runs up the road, turns right then left and arrives outside the hotel, just a little out of breath. Now he is worried once again – Frances is a terror. He enters.

'Hi, did a package come for room 21?' he says mustering all the chirp he can.

'Yeah, we sent it up,' comes the response; although Vinnie can only see the tops of two bowed heads and doesn't know who spoke. 'The delivery guy looked like he was crying when he left.' The words fill him with horror.

He dashes past and up the creaking stairs; he pretty much knows where all of the fifteen rooms are in this 'atmospheric retreat', having charged the atmosphere in most of them at some time or other. He reaches 21; he listens at the door; that can't be a ventilator he hears, surely? His hands are trembling visibly – he is not digging this gig. He closes his eyes, draws a deep breath and throws himself to the dog. After his knock the silence seems endless, he is about to knock again . . .

'Next time I told you I will get you in the eye with my hypo, you little shit.'

Vinnie gulps. 'Frances darling, it's Vinnie,' he says as quietly and soothingly as he can. 'I know you need your privacy, but I need that package; it is completely my fault.' He tries to sound as contrite as he can.

'I'll send round Pascal tomorrow; he will be totally at your disposal, my darling. I just need you to open the door and give me the package now, if you can?'

The door cracks open, out hurtles the package. It's been opened, ripped and even chewed by the looks of it. The door slams shut.

'Make sure you send Pascal at 4 p.m. exactly!'

Vinnie feels relieved. Thank God! She is obviously on painkillers and they've taken off her edge.

*　*　*

Back at the desk, Vinnie is finally beginning to relax.

He has left a message for Jeff telling him he has his package and he has Connery's luggage safely by his side. What could possibly go wrong now . . . ?

Jeff Perry returns and approaches the desk; with no words Vinnie hands him the dishevelled package. Jeff tears open what's left to be torn, and reads the contents. Lauren and Vinnie, both frozen to their spots, are watching Jeff intently. He reads the sheet and within seconds, without a word, his neck swells, he bursts into tears and runs off into the Soho night. Vinnie turns to Lauren, who, unable to help herself, begins to giggle.

'What was that all about?'

'Gawd knows, was it tears of joy or despair?'

The phone rings interrupting their chain of thought.

'Vinnie darling, someone wants a word . . . '

Minho Kwon – Harpy

The Harpies

Not so far away from Soho and not so long ago, there were five girls from different walks of life. Some had met in their late teens, but they all had one thing in common; they were a bunch of spoilt, nasty little bitches who bullied everyone they could.

The self-proclaimed leader of this gang is a household name, a famous supermodel known the world over as W. W was discovered in her early teens at a bus station and was thrust underage straight into the spotlight of the modelling world, which now pretends to have cleaned up its act. She refused to study in the manner of Queen Victoria; if she didn't get what she wanted she threw tantrums and whatever else was to hand. She has behaved like that ever since. Some say that one of the reasons that she is known as simply W is because she never learnt to spell; she can usually remember how to write her *nom de plume*, but has been known to sign autographs with the letter S or even C. W is, however, stunningly beautiful, and that is a fact. She is a little short perhaps by classic standards, but love her, like her or hate her, she is undeniably a beauty, although the kind that should only be seen in magazines, not one to one in a living, breathing encounter.

W's sidekick, Georgina Mutt, is far from an archetypal beauty. She is a little plump, has jet-black hair cut into an asymmetric bob and wears very badly applied heavy make-up. Her father was a little bit of a crook, although not a very good one. Her mother had delusions of grandeur and was a world-famous clairvoyant, although she could barely make tea, let alone read its leaves. Georgina grew up in dresses that were far too tight, used to her mother's tales of doom and destruction and the many cups that were smashed in the saucer from abortive tealeaf readings. Georgina was quick-witted and very swiftly turned to instant coffee and never went back. Now, out of the five girls, Georgina is the nastiest of all. From her adolescence to the present day, if she wants something, she takes it, be it clothes, make-up, jewellery or men. She has, as it were, taken the skirts off other girls' backs and made them walk home in their knickers. She has taken other girls' boyfriends, and then told the guys falsely that she is pregnant just to see the petrified look on their faces. And when she dumps them, she is famous for saying in a very common accent, 'At the end of the cunting day it's night, and you can fuck right off.'

Marina Singer, the lesbian lover of both W and Georgina Mutt, has no personality of her own and does everything she is told, which is the only reason she is a friend of the other two. She is not really a lesbian at all, merely good at obeying orders. An actress, she once had a part in an appallingly bad soap. Her character was killed off. She did go back on set the next day but only on the instructions of W and Georgina, who fell about laughing at her stupidity. Marina Singer is very pretty, but rather hard-looking. She married a Formula One driver, as it was the only thing that she could do. She never talks to anybody – she thinks it's because she's being mysterious but the fact is she has nothing to say. And W and Georgina have told her not to utter a sound. She will only talk to people if they will do her favours or if they are celebrities. She is, out of all the five girls, the most instantly forgettable.

Ruby Mist on the other hand is in competition with W for leadership of the gang; there is an unspoken rivalry between them, although why anybody would wish to be in this gang is beyond the rest of us, but, hey, such is life. Ruby is famous for showing off her ample, heaving breasts in B movies and period dramas. She did marry well but that ended in divorce. She did even better out of that and became a lady who lunches, or is that a bitch that sprays? Denying her advancing years, she is the oldest of the gang; she takes young lovers thinking it will keep her young. Some suggest that perhaps she drinks their pee. She carries her own Botox-injection kit for top-ups during the night and her behaviour is like that of the three others: spoilt, nasty and childlike.

Sally Braithwaite, the youngest and newest of this sadistic clan, is very much under

Ruby's wing. Poor little but extremely rich girl, Sally was forced to buy a property in the same street where they all live over lunch one day. Ruby said it would be such a good idea because then they wouldn't have to bother with taxis; after all, the fewer trades-people you talk to the better. Sally, lazy at heart (the reason why she is fat), jumped up, marched into the nearest estate agency and bought a place with cash. Sally Braithwaite is from a famous family of ballad singers, like the Von Trapps but without the fun. Sally is famous for smashing her guitar while blasting out Karen Carpenter classics and Sally really shouldn't sing Karen Carpenter seeing she's at least a size sixteen. The only reason this fat girl is allowed to be in the gang is the fact that she makes the others look slimmer, sexier and more beautiful. And they love rubbing it in, how much older they are and how much better they look.

So, that's the introduction to our famous five. Let's leave the North London hillside which they all call home and let's go out with them for a night on the town in one of their favourite hotspots, Soho.

Our harpies are now swaggering down the cobbles of Meard Street, on the lookout for victims to bully. W stops to look at a gentleman's jacket in the shop window of John Pearce. He has tailored, among many others, Mick, Keith, Bill and Charlie, even Brian. She turns her beautiful face in the direction of her gang; they stop dead except for Ruby, who looks tonight like Snow White on mushrooms. Ruby walks to the end of the street and lights up a fag, looking at everyone as though she despises them – which is pretty much the truth. Georgina grabs Sally, telling her to look at the jacket in the shop window. W speaks with a helium-enhanced high-octave screech, which sends the cats, dogs and Soho rats into hiding.

'What do you think of this jacket, girls?'

'Oh, W, I just love it! You'll look fantastic in it.'

Georgina glares in the direction of Marina and barks, 'You stupid dozy whore's cunt, it's for, erm . . . what's the name of the bloke you're going out with again?'

W takes a moment. 'What day is it? I think it's that record-producer guy, can't think of his name just now.'

W turns away, never to see the jacket again, slowly followed by Marina and Georgina, leaving Sally still trying to figure out what they are talking about.

Marina clasps her hands together. 'Oh I love that producer guy, I thought you looked so fab together.'

Georgina screws up her already screwed-up face and growls, 'For fuck's sake, for the love of God, you never met the wanker.'

Marina just looks upset and bewildered by this; although Marina does think that she has met everyone, she is often a little confused.

All the girls except Sally are now at the corner of Meard Street, having caught up with Ruby, who has just flicked her fag in the direction of a beautiful lady's flowing skirt. Ruby's aim was bull's-eye and the unfortunate woman's skirt went straight up in flames. Ruby has not felt so triumphant since her divorce ruling. Sally has given up studying her reflection in the tailor's window and, slightly out of breath, catches up with the rest of the gaggle. They cross the road, more *Dodge City* than *Sex and the City*, enter the newly opened members' club in Karl Marx's old digs on the other side of Dean Street and head straight to the VIP pen, walking past the rather too demure reception girls without even a glance in their direction.

For these A-list bully girls, jealousy is their cocktail, their fragrance, their couture, their way of life. The inside of their newest territory is extremely decadent, elegantly mixing colours and textures. Walking down the stairs the girls bump into Queenie, another beautiful girl, the daughter of a beauty queen and a diamond smuggler. Queenie always wears a huge diamond ring on her index finger, her only inheritance, and all that was left of her father. Her old mother is now in a padded cell, thanking everyone that she comes into contact with, telling them she would love to open a hospice for sick animals. That one has definitely lost her mind.

Queenie, whose birth name is Elizabeth, is famous for spinning vinyl in a digital age. But she is even more famous for her thousand and more shoes. Once, in an interview with a common fashion rag, Queenie confessed that she would love to wear all of the shoes at the same time. She has never quite lived that one down.

They greet each other like long-lost enemies and all smile sweetly with a side order of sneer. Moving swiftly past, W stops and with her five-year-old's voice squeaks, 'How are your babies? Do you still see the fathers?'

'Sorry, W darling, I would hate to stop and chat, so I won't,' and with that Queenie is just another memory of the night.

Going up the stairs Marina, whose pencil skirt was made for a one-legged anorexic teenager, finds it so hard to walk that Georgina has to pretty much carry her.

Sally, who is puffing and red-faced, manages breathlessly to ask who Queenie is. Ruby replies, 'She's the daughter of a glamour model who flipped her lid. She's become a B-list DJ who's got knocked up twice, firstly by one of those Manc brothers, then by that jailbird junkie W fucked for a while. So that's her pension sorted. Game, set and snatch.'

Marina looked at Sally nodding. 'Yes we all hate Queenie, that one would have done absolutely anything to have become famous.' Georgina clenched her fist, closed her eyes, then smiled and said through gritted teeth, 'And you, sweetheart, married a racing driver.'

They all walk over to Max, who owns this place with his brother Fred. Max, like Fred, is short and stout, but while Fred is serious, Max is more of the court jester. He greets the girls like long-lost little angels, but knows they are more like the witches in *Macbeth*, maybe worse. After a round of false pleasantries and a load of free booze, the girls notice Sabrina Taylor walk through the ever-opening door. Sabrina glides over towards Max, who by this point is doing cartwheels and singing Pavarotti's top ten hits to his audience in the mirror.

'Girls!' Sabrina says not looking at any of them. 'How awful to see you all at the same time. Sally, darling child, have you ever seen *Rosemary's Baby*? No? Well you really should.'

She continues on her way to have a little gossip with Max who has finished his chart countdown and is now clapping his hands and jumping up and down chuckling over his own jokes. Just as Sabrina is about to embrace Max, W squeaks up, 'How's your latest chick flick, Sab honey? I see you're still wearing last season's gear . . . must be because you're so busy, hon?'

'W darling, I don't make lesbian films. However, if I do get offered any of them I will definitely pass them your way – after all, you've already done plenty of research. Must go, I have a plane to catch. You remember work, don't you . . . ? Oh well, maybe not.' Saying goodbye only to Max, Sabrina is gone.

Ruby pipes up, 'Fucking bitch.'

Just then Georgina's mobile beeps with an invite to the latest hot street artist's party, complete with top-secret location and invites by text only. The girls leave; no money changes hands for their refreshments – not ever. Without even saying goodbye, off they go to the newly revealed secret location – an old car park behind Glasshouse Street that is just about to be bulldozed in the name of progress. All the top artists are there, as well as fire-breathing entertainers, jugglers and trapeze acts. The girls insult anybody who comes their way and ignore anyone who tries to talk to them.

Marina, who is looking puzzled and whose skirt is beginning to give her stomach cramps because it is so tight, turns her head in the direction of W, and asks what the point of this party is. For once without squeaking, W just shrugs her shoulders. Georgina, never one to miss a trick, spouts her usual tirade of abuse in Marina's face. Ruby decides to step in and educate the girls about the goings on around town.

'Darlings, remember we are gathered here tonight among all the greatest living artists. Look around you, all those you will have heard of are here. Tonight is the début of their latest discovery, and wait till you see him, ladies, he is quite a catch.'

As she finishes she turns to see that funny little twosome who always seem to be at these dos. Well one of them at least is a funny little thing, in his pinstripe suit and patent shoes; his sidekick is probably a little too tall to be seen next to him, but they make quite a sight.

The little one announces his presence with a shriek of agreement, while throwing his arms open wide rather like a Wagnerian soprano. 'Oh my God, he's beautiful, he's amazing; he is simply sensational. He is just like a Roman god – with more talent.'

Georgina spins around, her head seeming to spin rather more than her torso, reminding those who notice such things a little too much of *The Exorcist*.

'Don't you mean Greek god, you stupid gay boy?'

'No, sweetheart, I don't, everyone is so bored with the Greeks, don't you know? The only people who aren't are the Cypriots and they're not really Greek.'

With that the twosome disappear into the crowd, the one disappearing quicker than the other.

The crowd starts to throb; devotees mob together as more and more of them seem to be arriving. Their focus is this latest deity, their frenzied anticipation making the air literally crackle. Vinnie isn't too far off; the Coliseum before the lions were let loose must have felt a little like this. Suddenly the urban arena falls silent. The trapeze stops swinging and hangs limply from its ropes. The jugglers allow their balls to drop; the fire breathers take a well-deserved swig of water. A man dressed in robes motions for the crowd to part: it does so without a murmur. Silence.

A loud pyrotechnic display showers the spectators in light of every colour. They respond with cheers and whoops, which bounce off the raw concrete walls, growing into a crescendo of noise. Out of this blinding explosion the image of a face appears, that of the idol that the crowd has been hungry for. The mirage smiles broadly and begins to speak; he introduces himself simply as Sam. The paroxysm of the crowd and the image of his loved one three storeys high is just too much for the funny little guy in the patent shoes and he drops in a faint to the dirty, dusty concrete floor. Realising he is out cold, Georgina puts in a sly stiletto to the groin and grins to herself.

A little farther over in the crowd, James has lost sight of his diminutive sidekick, and while looking around he feels a tug at his elbow from, as it transpires, a little fat hand.

'Do you know anything about *Rosemary's Baby . . . ?*'

*Tim Noble and
Sue Webster –
Wedding Napkin*

Some Stories are Warnings to Us All; Sweet Suzie's is Definitely One of Them

On a farmstead deep in the Australian outback, far away from the hedonistic streets of Soho, lived a close and loving family. Suzie, the middle of three girls, dreamt of other things than the farmers' never-ending talk of rainfall and pasture; she longed to get away from the endless horizons and unrelenting sunshine, to find a place far removed from the harsh world into which she had been born, where the men were always men and the women did as they were told.

Petite, with flame hair and fresh, freckled, milky skin that betrayed her Irish roots, Suzie had no way of knowing how attractive she really was. She was more than a bit of a tomboy, never showed off her body and didn't seem to have much luck with the guys, although given the gene pool she had to choose from, that was hardly surprising. On her first date with Grant, her boyfriend for over a year, she had found him rifling down the back of her parents' sofa looking for lost change. This should have alerted her, but she had her insecurities like the best of us, and thought it was better to date than to be alone. She had only recently summoned up the courage to dump him.

She made friends easily though, as she was smart and funny. Her grandmother had been well known in the district as an entertainer and Suzie took after her. She may have been a little quirky and something of an oddball, but her Celtic wit was quick and infectious and she had made some great friends whom she would miss terribly if she ever did get away – but she knew she had to.

Two years after leaving high school she was still working in the offices of the Livestock Marketing Centre because there was almost nowhere else she could work.

She saved every cent she could, spent little and worked on the farm and around the house at weekends to pay for her room and board.

Suzie's parents, despite their concerns, had long become accustomed to the idea that she was going to travel. Like so many of their friends' children, she had an overwhelming desire to explore and experience all the world could offer. Rural New South Wales may have been the place she called home, but they knew the link was tenuous and hoped that, for her, getting away would be the best thing she could do. They told themselves it would be an amazing opportunity for her to be able finally to grow up and find out who she really was.

So after two years of scrimping and a month after she had finished with Grant she was ready to ditch the farm and the endless sweeping of the red dirt off the verandah each morning. She spent her last night with her two best friends, Donna and Melissa, getting drunk, gazing up at the familiar southern sky, full of stars, and knowing how different it would look on the other side of the world.

The following morning she grabbed her rucksack and headed for the airport.

She was just a few weeks into her twenty-first year when she emerged a day and a half later into the throng at King's Cross Station. As she threaded herself through the daunting mass of people and scanned the crowds for Gareth, a friend of her cousin's who had made the escape two years before and who had promised to meet her, she realised this was unlike anything she had ever experienced and the prospect of what lay ahead was thrilling. Gareth had got a place for her at one of the backpacker houses favoured by young Antipodeans that can be found scattered right across London. Suzie had a bed in a room she shared with some other young girls who had set off on adventures of their own and she spent her first night in the house in Stoke Newington sitting up to talk with her new friends about trips to Paris, Rome, Barcelona, Berlin and Istanbul.

That night a combination of jet lag and excitement kept Suzie awake until the weak spring sunlight made its first appearance. She had an interview that afternoon in the West End with an ex-bar manager of Gareth's who was putting together a team for some new venue just off Piccadilly Circus that was having a 'soft' opening within a few days.

She killed the hours before this meeting wandering through central London, feeling the city's vibrations. By three-fifteen Suzie had found her way to the entrance of the venue on the edge of Soho, totally unaware of how its deco glamour was destined to take London's nightlife by storm. By four she was back out the door, job sorted, mission accomplished. Her first trial shift was the following night. The bar manager, an ex-soap actor, was friendly in a melancholy way. He had played a doctor in a long-standing rural soap opera, but tragically had been killed off as his hairline receded; that was the beginning of the end of acting, his first career, and the start of his second one.

Suzie was set. Work, rest and, very quickly, play. Soon enough her shifts began ending in the early hours and her body clock responded. Within a few weeks she had moved out of Stokey and got her own room near Old Street, in a shared flat with two friends whom she had met at work. It quickly became quite a co-dependent little group. One, Craig, became her constant companion. They would spend cosy evenings reading in her bed on their infrequent nights off – in fact doing pretty much every-thing a couple might do, but never admitting it. Fiona, their other flatmate, skinnier than an Ashtanga yoga teacher on a strict vegan diet, was always teasing the two of them about their connection, but as far as they were concerned they were just good friends.

A combination of hard work, common sense and an excellent memory meant she soon became an invaluable member of staff at the Pacific. When calamity struck, as it sometimes did, she was often the one who saved the day and it was she who took on the job of showing new staff the ropes, teaching them the skills to make everyone's night go a little smoother.

With gathering pace, the weeks became months; summer kicked in with a vengeance that year, and soon the nights seemed to go on for ever. Recreation combined with workload and it sometimes became difficult to tell night from day, or was that day from night? No one worried, it was all part of the fun.

Night after night was spent out socialising with colleagues at one or more of the many late-night haunts hidden in various basements in the West End and designed to cater for both club workers and party people who wouldn't or couldn't go home – not yet. One night the threesome found they all had a rare night off together. This seemed as good a reason as any to celebrate; cocktails were in order. Craig phoned a friend who worked the front desk of a particularly glamorous club and soon they were on their way.

Occasionally, a real A-lister would pitch up, but not all that often. Luckily that night the club manager, an old colleague of Craig's, was on duty, so by 10 p.m. the three of them found themselves on a table at the club next to the one English movie star able to open a movie – even if only a bad remake of a 1960s' cult film. In fact, his whole table was littered with young Brit actors talking over each other. Suzie and company raised their espresso Martinis, 'the only legal lift', to their lips, celebrating their good fortune in being right in the midst of where it was all at, in the most exclusive club, in the centre of the most exciting city in the world. Things could hardly get better.

As if on cue the buxom manager who made this all possible appeared. She untied her hair, Salon Select style, while telling the gang how great they were all looking. She never once took her eyes off her own reflection in the wall mirror framed in the panelled wall the whole time she spoke, making sure that her hair was falling bouncily over her shoulders and that her recently reapplied lipstick had not smeared across her teeth. Squeak squeak. Without waiting for them to reply she was off to the next table for some more complimenting.

'Hey, gang, what's your plan tonight?' The trio turned to see Lauren, another of Craig's old friends and one of the gaggle of part-timers who worked on the front desk. 'You know our crazy host is having one of his discos upstairs tonight? It's just about to start; give it an hour or so and it will be pumping. You know that actress Karen Stein? She usually ends up topless on the dance floor crying for attention or spitting on you if you get too close; it'll be fun!'

Suzie, listening to all this, was still a little mesmerised by her surroundings. Part of her still found it hard to believe that just a few months ago she was kicking hot red dust for fun. So many of the faces were people she recognised, although she couldn't quite name them, and the dimly seductive lighting flattered even the most florid of complexions. Everyone seemed larger than life, including the waiters on the make, swishing up and down the room looking for a break. The waitresses were doing pretty much the same and one of them appeared to be wearing no underwear at all (Suzie had glimpsed more than she cared to when the girl leant over a table of middle-aged producer types). One of them, comfortable in his usual spot, chewing on an unlit cigar, drank his Martini with one hand, while his other was lost under her mini, mini skirt, caressing her secret.

The sound of chatter bounced off the walls, the palpable frenzy of networking all adding to the seductive energy of this celebrity hang-out. Suzie privately celebrated her first three months in town. If only her old friends Donna and Melissa, back in New South Wales, could see her now! This outback girl done good, she thought, although she realised guiltily it had been ages since she had been in touch with them. During her first weeks she had kept them updated with e-mails detailing every twist and turn of her new life; recently she had told them nothing. Her life here in London had taken over; she seemed never to have the time or inclination to sit and write her missives any more. She really should get in touch . . .

After more drinks, more chats and more drinks again, they grabbed their glasses and headed upstairs to the seasonal disco, recently described on some celebrity gossip blog as *the* place where the famous faces get a little crazy.

Earth, Wind and Fire were pumping out their fantasy as they entered the room. The DJ that night was Sonny, whom the crazy host always booked because he had been in love with him (or so he claimed) for ten years or more. On the other side of the room chatting up her new latest best friend – that's what she always does best – was the DJ's wife. By day, a weather girl, a party girl by night. A Scandinavian Grace Kelly lookalike, she was holding up well for her years and in the flashing lights she still looked hot.

'Hi, you must be the cats Lauren's dragged in from the rain.' It was the host, Vinnie, arm in arm with Lauren who had finished with the desk for the night. 'I do hope you're enjoying my Summer Disco Ball!'

Fiona began gushing over Vinnie in response. Suzie, as usual, was scanning the room, determined to remember it all. Craig never spoke much.

'The strong and silent type, are you? Just my cup of tea.' Vinnie turned his attention towards Craig (for a moment), pouring on his charm. 'I simply adore that shirt, but you know what I adore more?'

'What?' Craig forced himself to reply.

'The man inside, of course,' Vinnie laughed, holding him by the chin and stroking it with a motion mysterious as a Mason's handshake. 'I must go, there's my absolute favourite over there. What's his name again, Lauren?' He disappeared into the crowd in a flash.

Craig was a kind soul, but found this kind of social interaction intimidating. Quite why he had done so well working behind bars in London no one could work out. The local library would have seemed more the place for him, but his dyslexia put paid to that.

A few hours later, as they were leaving with Lauren, now making up a foursome, they saw Vinnie locked in a tight embrace with the DJ, whispering furtively in his ear.

It was a little after 2 a.m. when they headed off, planning to have one last drink at another club just around the corner, a club for the younger trust-fund crowd who quite frankly were pretty tiresome to party with. But it was licensed till three, and the cocktails were strong and by the time they fell down the stairs and out the door they felt like the new stars in town.

'Come on,' Lauren suggested, 'let's go to Tom's; its a bit of a dive but what the hell, we're having such a good night.'

Tom's is a little doorway just off the main drag. If you ring the right buzzer, a disconnected voice will quiz you about your credentials for entry. Only a handful of people are members, just enough to keep Westminster Council happy. For the rest it's a question of whether you're in the know or have the right name to mention to get you buzzed in. Lauren knew her job and they descended the stairs into a room not much bigger than a bedsit. A bar is to one side and a variety of mismatched wooden tables and chairs complete the décor. The clientele? Not unlike that at the bar in *Star Wars*. The staff look desperately in need of vitamin D, a square meal, a hot shower and bed.

The manager is so tired and confused he doesn't know whether he wants to go home to his wife or home with Vinnie, who is already holding court and attempting to mesmerise yet another married man, the only type of man he put any effort into seducing. As he never tired of saying, 'I adore married men – you get to give them back.' Once on a radio talkshow, in answer to a question about the difference between straight men and gay men, he had responded to the DJ, whom he had felt up just days before, 'I can't quite think . . .'

After an hour or so at Tom's, Lauren suggested moving on. She was bored there; there were no men she was interested in, and besides Vinnie had informed her that her dealer of choice was at Aphrodite's with treats.

Leaving Tom's, by now definitely a little the worse for wear, they head over, bracing themselves against the chill of the early-morning air.

On a parallel street stood Aphrodite's, a landmark late-night drinking den situated in the basement of a sex shop which you had to go through to gain entry. As it didn't even open till 3 a.m., the staff were usually still clearing up at noon. Those who worked there were generally ex-staff from nearby clubs who had been recently fired for some kind of indiscretion.

If Tom's was like the bar in *Star Wars*, Aphrodite's was the bar in purgatory, the only barman looking like Nosferatu's first cousin. As the place filled up, witches and ghouls descended into the space. Lauren, a hardened regular, was lifted after a brief interaction with the man she came to find.

By now Craig has begun to feel completely out of his depth, and realising that he hasn't seen Suzie since they first arrived, corners Lauren to find out if she knows where she might have gone.

'Chill out, dude, she's been here before, she knows what she's doing,' Lauren shouts back over the loud and tinny music.

But he is beginning to have a bad feeling; perhaps it's because he is not nearly such a dipper as the girls, or perhaps it's just a bad batch. He finds himself being ranted at by a woman not only foaming at the mouth but from every visible orifice.

Lauren, peaking, needs to keep moving. Fiona hears of an underground party and the two of them scarper. Craig stays, he needs to find Suzie. By now he is really anxious; it's probably just the drugs he tells himself when his heart begins to race and a feeling of dread washes over him. He convinces himself she must have been feeling the same and left without him noticing. Suzie has begun to try quite a lot of things in her short time in town, but is still very much a novice. He is sure now that he will find her back home, and leaves. By the time he has walked back to their flat, he will have calmed down and Suzie will be there, tucked up safely in bed.

Meanwhile, the truth of the matter is that Suzie had felt rather under the weather, but instead of leaving she had gone to the toilet to try and compose herself. She had waited outside, thinking that the door was locked when it had refused to budge. After a few minutes she tried it again, this time it gave; she must have been mistaken; this was always happening to her. Stepping inside she peered through the gloom at the dingy little room containing a WC, a filthy sink and a foul stench. Before she had the chance to close the door behind her, a figure appeared in the doorway.

'You all right, baby?'

Suzie was a little unnerved. She was feeling edgy; the cheap Soho drugs were beginning to wear off.

'You're looking a little lost. You need a sharpener.' He was smooth and smiled easily. Suzie thought she recognised him. Wasn't he the guy Lauren had been talking and laughing with earlier? Compared to most of the crowd here, he looked together and unaffected by drugs.

He eased his way into the tiny room, and found the light switch. The fluorescent glow was harsh, highlighting every flaw and follicle. As the door latch clicked behind him he held a bump gun to her nostril and fired it. His own personal stash, cleaner than the shit he sold, gave Suzie an instant high; she felt much better.

'You think that's good? I've got something to make you feel even better.' Suzie now felt in control, very aware of what was going on, enjoying the moment. She smiled, she was up for it.

He pressed a small pipe against her lips. As he lit the other end, he told her to suck slowly and hold it in, then let it out slowly; expertly tutoring her in this act.

This rush hits her instantly. She has never felt so awake, so alive and happy. This is the most amazing time of her life; she hugs her tutor.

'Here, suck it again, babe, slowly; hold it in,' he repeats this a few more times, holding her head as she draws deeper and deeper on the glowing crystals. Finally Suzie is so overwhelmed with the intensity, she stops, closes her eyes and leans back, consumed with this moment.

'Dirty bitch.' She feels a force against her, is pushed against the filthy whitewashed wall. She tries to focus, but it's impossible, she's too far gone, her synapses can't connect. All she feels is a burning sensation from her abuse of the pipe. An intense white noise is almost exploding in her head. Fear and panic rise, but she is near to passing out.

He has her pinned within his massive hands, the weight of his bulked-up body too great to fight. In a flash he rips from her lower body the skirt she recently bought just for a special night out, then he tears off her pants, tearing at the skin on her thighs with his nails. The scarlet blood is startling in the white light; she manages to look down and sees it, is transfixed by it, but the pain is fleeting. He then puts his hand over her mouth to prevent her screaming, but Suzie has no scream within her, she is drifting in and out of consciousness. He forces his free hand into her, another pain she feels. Confused, tears begin to fall down her face, her body is going into shock, letting go of any pain.

He flips her round sharply; she is like a rag doll in his grip. His hand is still clamped to her mouth jerking her head back, almost snapping her neck. Her face smashes up against the wall. Finished in seconds, he lets Suzie drop, picks up her torn clothes and wipes himself off with them. He spits at her, 'I'm coming back for you,' and then he smiles almost sweetly. Finally he slaps her so hard across the face that this time she does pass out.

He turns out the light as he leaves.

Many hours later the staff find her curled up in the corner beneath the basin, and manage to get her up. The manageress, a professional musician between gigs, well used to cleaning up the mess after nights at Aphrodite's, gives her coffee. She tries to get her to talk, but Suzie will say nothing, so she drops her off in Old Street on her way home; she hopes that nothing will be said and that no scandal will come of this.

Three months and an abortion later, Suzie is no longer living with Craig and Fiona. Or working at the Pacific. One night after finishing her late shift, Lauren spots Suzie ducking into Bourchier Street – piss alley. For a moment she feels tremendous guilt, but convinces herself that Suzie is beyond her help now. Lauren's heart races at the thought of the miserable existence Suzie now lives. She wants to go and help, but everyone has told her it's no use. Craig had spent weeks trying; he'd even got the police involved, although they were really not at all interested. But she can't just drive off, she has to go and see once again if she can help; convince Suzie to let her take her home, give her some space, get her away from these ghouls.

Lauren walks to the end of the alley, and sees Suzie on her knees with some grubby old man wanking himself off into her waiting open mouth. Lauren retches, turns and rushes to her car and begins to cry once she is safely back behind the wheel.

As she pulls away she spies her old dealer sitting in his car a little up the street, knowing he is Suzie's pimp. The pimp and the crack whore. He and his gang had had their fun with Suzie for a few weeks but soon got bored with her and her ever increasing demands for drugs, coupled with her ever diminishing charms. Suzie had lost all she ever had. Her skin no longer milky, just ghostly, her red hair dull, greasy and limp. She would do anything and anyone for the price of a hit. The phone box up the road had become her office. She would fight off the local tramp who used it as his home so she could smoke her pipe in peace.

This pimp, her ruination, was the end of the line for Suzie. She was beyond selling, finished. Eventually he and his posse beat her so badly she never walked quite upright again. Afterwards, they kicked her out, warned her never to come near or they'd cut her up. They'd fuck anything, but they could only be seen with fit birds.

A month or so later she was only able to trick with the homeless guys who would give her some of their crack. The sores on her face didn't seem to bother them. When she needed to eat she went to Berwick Street. Round the back were always a box or two of putrid vegetables and fruit. She couldn't taste anything anyway, only felt the need to feed her face.

One cold wet morning, the homeless guy with whom she shared the phone box's facilities went for breakfast at the same place and found her even paler than usual. He tried to wake her, and then realised the pavement around her was stained with blood, her body was punctured like a pincushion. The coroner later revealed sixteen stab wounds were counted on her pale, shrunken body. Most blows came before she died.

She was three days short of her twenty-first birthday. Always was a big party for that, but not for Suzie.

Some Stories are Warnings to Us All; Sweet Suzie's is Definitely One of Them

Rachel Howard –
Fly in the Ointment

The Flamingo Bar and Grill;
The Return of Disco

What people often don't realise is that Soho is a village. Its narrow streets are unlike anywhere else in London. In all villages, everyone thinks they're hip to everybody's business, but as in all villages, the fact is they're not. Of course most of the locals in this village are mere daytime inhabitants who spend most of their waking hours in these winding streets working or wheeling and dealing, often only leaving the place for a few hours to sleep in their beds in outlying areas. The local residents are few, and that makes them very protective of this square half-mile, bang in the middle of this glorious city. These characters often seem like caricatures, extreme forms of people in other parts of the country; to survive the streets here demands a confidence that is not at all the norm. But where did these locals come from? Who were they before they became who they are today? Who were they yesterday?

A few years back, when Soho was beginning its latest reinvention, the one that continues to this day, a place opened that catered to all sorts of these Soho natives, these caricatures. Strictly speaking, it was in fact just out of the village limits, on the wrong side of the tracks, west of Regent Street. A quick streak across the road from the northern edge of Soho takes you down towards a surprisingly genteel square to the south west of Oxford Circus. Before the square reveals itself fully, a small black door on the left was for a short period of time entrance to that holiest (in these parts), of holy grails, the best little disco ever. London's very own spatially-challenged Studio 54.

There was nostalgia in the air; *Saturday Night Fever* was on re-runs and hip with a crowd too young to have seen it first time round. Studio 54 itself was the subject of books and movies. A number of the Soho crowd claimed to have been there, but it was usually only in their imagination. Disco was hot; everyone wanted to dance.

Dick, who set it up with investors and managed the place, was at the time quite the most famous landlord in Soho, but being the most famous landlord in Soho was not quite the same as in Chipping Camden. It is not about your ales and pies, but about your cocktails, your cute staff, the music, lights, high heels, cleavage and hairdos. Well, at least night-time Soho is, although these days daytime Soho seems rather unhealthily obsessed with ales and pies – British rustic, don't you know.

Back then Dick Bradsell was making quite a name for himself by opening one hot new bar after another, having previously managed the second of the late-twentieth-century round of great members' clubs known simply by the founder's first name: Fred or rather Fred's. It was the one that never survived, economies of scale anyone who knew it might suspect.

This new place was physically rather similar; you know the scene, entrance down a grubby flight of steps leading to a bar on one side with a rather narrow area in front, beyond which the room opened up. Because this place had once been a slightly seedy late-night gay bar in the days when Westminster Council allowed bars for gay men who didn't want to drink cocktails, the rear of the club was surprisingly cavernous. There was space for a dance floor ringed with benches and small tables and chairs. At the far end a few curving steps rose to an elevated platform. The place had something of a Hollywood feel, a grungy miniature Coconut Club if you like. It was possible to imagine some torch singer seducing the crowd gathered around tables drinking. Think of that, but with the tables pushed back, the whiny singer chucked off the stage and a DJ pumping out the tunes, and pile on the drugs, and you'll have a pretty good picture of the place.

Dick was quite a character; his face was a little foxy and rather stern and he had wildly disparate skills. As well as being a Black Belt at Kung Fu, he transformed into a mean Baby Jane – the one near the end of the movie, but without her letters to daddy; she was such good fun she came to work in the evenings a fair bit. Under his guidance the Flamingo Bar and Grill was an instant success; the atmosphere thick with fun and games, the set-up near perfect for such a place.

The door was watched over by Danny, a legend among Soho's doormen. He stood close to seven feet tall, or so it seemed, and had a naturally rather kind face, which he could screw up into a fearsome scowl at the first sign of trouble. Although when you're the size he is, no one ever takes you on. He had never once had a fight; a quick 'in yer face' from someone that big would reduce anyone to a mere rabbit in the headlights.

He worked at the street-level entrance in the lobby alongside the door whore, Cass. Cass had worked all across Soho, starting east and ending up here in the far west. Her first gig had been on Old Compton Street and had been a riot, and the beginning of her infamy, from start to finish. She had had to go when her illegal parties that began half an hour after the place had closed for the night started to attract a little too much police attention. Cass was famous for her thousand looks. While her outfits were more like exotic costumes than the normal party frocks that the trust-fund kids wore, her conversation was straight from the gutter.

At the foot of the narrow stairs was a small reception area, with a desk adorned with a beautiful young woman, Freddie. By day she studied for another sort of Bar. Her figure was incredibly shapely, lithe, the kind all men loved. No matter what time of the night, she could always be found encircled by guys offering her drinks and cigarettes. It never worked though, she didn't smoke and hardly drank. So those offers became offers of holidays, even marriage; she always just laughed them off, because what these men didn't know was that she was deeply in love with Sandra; they had been together about six months at that point. The pair ended up running away together. Sandra's family refused to admit, far less accept, their beloved daughter was a lesbian. They ran to New York. Today they are one of New York's most feared legal teams.

In one corner of this foyer was a small black doorway bisected with a narrow shelf behind which lay the cloakroom. One night Vinnie, our omnipresent Soho pro, still quite a newcomer to the village – remember he was only in his twenties then – was giving Freddie a hand with the coats. Feeling bored and with a mischievous need to be a little mean with the punters, they decided on that cold February night to charge two pounds per item. The pair of them left in the early hours with four hundred pounds from their little coup. At one point in the night, a customer decided to complain to the manager about the excessive charges. Vinnie disappeared into the club and returned with the best-dressed friend he could find; they got away with it once again.

*   *   *

Entering our holy place, behind that small bar to the left was Gareth, a wizard with the cocktail mixes. He often forgot to speak, but with a face like his, it could be forgiven. He was a young, much smoother version of Harrison Ford with thick grown-out hair. His colleague, Murray, was the new kid on the block, fresh-faced and gorgeous, a native of Dorset and better looking than most male models. It was difficult not to be a little concerned for the poor boy's safety, but Dick kept a close, watchful eye as he was a relative. He had something of Michael York about him, so as you can imagine, while the boys were hanging out around Freddie, this was where the girls hung out. These boys were young and flooded with testosterone; when the crowd got really thick and the heavy glances from the girls thicker, their mixing skills were lost in a flurry of competition as to who could knock out the most drinks while pocketing the most numbers.

Working the floor was Vinnie, our diminutive cocktail waiter with delusions of grandeur, and his co-worker Carol. She was addicted to ketamine and Toilet Duck – what she did with the Toilet Duck no one ever knew or wanted to get into with her. Even though they were definitely a rather debauched crowd, there were some things even they were a little squeamish about and, quite frankly, Carol was often beyond the pale.

One of the great sights of the Flamingo was what seemed to be a suspended serving tray that would appear and shimmy just over the crowd's heads, like a rather small and out-of-whack flying saucer, whenever 'Shine On' came on, which was every night twice a night. As this spinning, flying tray got nearer, the crowd beneath would part a little and Vinnie would finally emerge, his arm stretched straight up over his head, tray with (and this the truly remarkable part) drinks full to the brim planted firmly on top of his open little hand. He would spin the tray down like Dean would spin Torvill and deposit the refreshments on the table in front of you.

Flawless.

The third waitress on the nights this disco bar got packed languished under the unlikely name of Bethune and was a morphine addict from South Wales, a prolific breeding ground for that kind of thing apparently. More often than not, she would get lost in the crowd at some point in the night, only to be discovered when the place had emptied, comatose beneath whichever table she had made her nest.

At the far end of the club was the DJ box and the regular DJ was always Sonny. He had known Vinnie from their previous workplace, the Pleasure Palace. Vinnie had fallen head over heels for Sonny, but sadly Sonny was married to a beauty whom he adored. So Vinnie, who loved the drama more than he could probably love anybody, loved from afar. The music that pumped was pure disco; it was all about the dance. That little place would get so packed that the crowd dancing would move as one, a giant rippling organism under a revolving light. The mix was incredible; the staff all thought they were at a party. Some poor girl from Bromley would be really trying to have her twenty-first-birthday party, but it would be a chain of disasters as the staff got ever more ripped and the music so loud no one could hear her scream, 'It's my party.' But you know what? In the end no one ever cared; the bulimic model would be chatting to some smartly dressed gangster, who would be buying drinks for the gay Aussie rugby player, who was being felt up by the club kid, who was handing out the pills to make everyone even happier.

This particular night a number of other locals were inside.

James, a lifelong pal of Vinnie's, who had encouraged him to come to town, was there with Toni who had known James since he was still at school. Vinnie always thought she was pretty cool; she looked a little like Kristin Scott Thomas, and she always seemed to have on a pair of Wayfarers.

They would pitch up every now and again to drink tequila, often dancing the night away if they got in the mood, and it was pretty easy to get hold of the mood in this place.

At various times that night James found Vinnie or Sonny on their hands and knees scratching around the DJ-booth floor poring over the 12-inch disks. He thought they were being very choosy with the music, but they were in fact looking for the wrap of mood they had dropped.

Because this wrap was gone, Vinnie instead popped a few Es; a while later, as these were kicking in, he wandered down the back corridor towards the kitchen. You could actually order food in those days – burgers, club sandwiches, all surprisingly good, although this luxury would quickly disappear: it was really only for the licence. Vinnie approached the kitchen; the music was still thumpingly loud even back here, and he could see a group of girls literally dancing around their bags on the kitchen floor next to the oven, high as kites and grateful for some space. He smiled as he glimpsed them through the serving hatch. As he entered the kitchen, he saw the chef slumped on the floor in the corner. Clearly the girls had been too out of it to see him, or if they had, hadn't worried. But what Vinnie realised when he bent down to check was that the chef had OD'd and was dead. To say his rising mood was shattered is putting it mildly. As he clutched his head trying to work out what to do in his sadly confused state, the girls screamed, 'Conga!' and they all disappeared through the doors to join the end of the conga line that had formed spontaneously and was slinking and twisting around the disco. The whole scene was bizarre, but the party kept rocking on.

Just then Bethune crawled out from under the kitchen sink where she had made her latest nest; she helped Vinnie as best she could, which was not really any help at all. They dragged the chef to a darker, less obvious place; Vinnie will always remember that bit of cardboard box stuck to Bethune's head the whole time.

He ran to Sonny for advice with his little problem with the chef. Vinnie was quite frazzled at this point. He was immensely comforted by Sonny's tight embrace, and somehow found himself talking about the awful Hawaiian shirt he had to wear for a uniform in this sea of finery; at this, Sonny grabbed Vinnie hard with both hands and very sternly announced in a voice stronger than that of Laurence Olivier's Hamlet, 'I solemnly promise you, Vinnie, some day soon you will wear the finest clothes from Paris and Milan. Don't you realise that, Vinnie?' With a few lasts sobs and splutters,

Vinnie nodded and they drew apart. Vinnie sat in silence for a short while, falling just that bit deeper in love. Many many years later when Vinnie was getting ready to go out to the Baftas he caught a glimpse of himself in the mirror. He remembered Sonny's words and smiling to himself he made a mental note to phone Sonny to book a disco.

Finally, Vinnie returned to the scene of the fatality only to find that the body had moved. Someone else must have found the chef and moved him yet again. Vinnie began to panic properly this time – maybe they were phoning the police right now. As he turned for the door something caught at his heels and he looked down, stepping straight on to the chef's hand as he did so. The junkie moaned and spluttered, puking up just a little bit. Vinnie ran back into the throng and pulling Toni into the middle of the floor began to dance with her, the two of them spinning, waving and bumping butts. That no-good addict! thought Vinnie, immensely relieved that he wasn't going to have to dispose of another body. He closed his eyes, threw back his head and smiled.

Shine On.

The most exciting time at the Flamingo Bar and Grill was at 3 a.m. when the club closed and most of the drinkers and dancers had jived out the door: that was when the real party began. If you were known or got the nod from someone who worked there you could join the select bunch who would stay in their seats and wait for the place to clear. Then the lights would go back down a little, the music would come on quieter and the after-hours would begin. Like all after-hours, where nothing is natural and everyone is their own chemical experiment, it really wasn't that interesting, those lucky few just thought it was, as they took more drugs to get higher – or, more likely, to bring them down.

Shortly before the cleaners arrived these wannabe Studio 54ers would put back on their shades to brave the daylight and scuttle home.

As the last few disappeared around a corner of the deserted and cold but sunlit streets of Soho, James and Toni found themselves wandering through Golden Square, trying to remember where Toni had left her Alfa. They had two hours to get down to Sussex for her daughter's school open day. Toni was meeting the teachers.

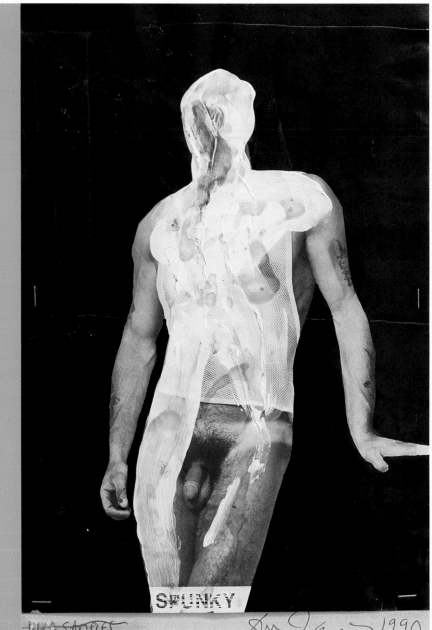

John Maybury – DNA

It's All Over 'cos the Fat Lady Can't Sing

Just as Tottenham Court Road is home to yesterday's analogue radio and today's digital systems, so Wardour Street is home to the production of motion pictures. Out of offices that are often rather too large and open plan, a throwback to the 1980s and 1990s (no one in their right mind creates these any more – where can you have an afternoon nap, for God's sake?), are spat some of the biggest blockbusters in town, as well as a few flops of course – usually films backed by government grants. Here is a rich tableau of high-powered board meetings, backstabbing and bareback fucking. Careers that begin on the couch and terminate at the Marie Stopes clinic. Secretaries who become wives, ex-wives who become heads of department. Husbands these days waking up in the morning next to husbands, what a wonderful modern world we live in.

Not far from that old pub the Bath House and just opposite St Anne's Court stands a squat, square building, home to a thumping great production company knocking out film after film. It is not unusual for Johnny Depp to be seen slipping out of the side door and straight into a limo. Outside the front door there is always a rather large gathering of young Brit actors, who just happen to be hanging around, hoping for the paps to spot them.

This building is one of a kind. It is the control centre for the whole shebang, headquarters to a company that has never once farmed out any of the production process; everything is handled in-house from the get-go.

Ground floor to one side is casting and opposite is the writing department, where curtains permanently closed to keep away the deadlines fail to muffle the sound of endless pacing.

First floor is for producers, junior to executive, and their PAs. When they're not raising money or fiddling with their secretary's knickers or on another fake phone call, they can be found at one of Soho's many members' clubs getting trashed: that might go on for days. As for the directors, who also work on the same floor, they are more likely to be found tugging on the few remaining follicles sprouting out of their ever reddening faces, stressed by their absent producers who never bother to tell them whether they have the money and are now nowhere to be found. They should try room 21 around the corner, they can usually be found there, queuing up, waiting for deliveries of provisions. They really should work on separate floors but the layout of this building will not allow such luxuries. It's rather short and stumpy – not unlike most producers – and ruled with a fist of iron by the tyranny that is Val Baker. She runs the show from beginning to end with her long-suffering, pathetic excuse of a husband, Gideon Baker.

Poor Gideon was frogmarched up the aisle by Val on their wedding day many, many moons ago. Her grip on his collar was so tight that some cruel wags joke that like a noose around his neck it in fact strangled Gideon and Val became a widow that very day. He was certainly totally silenced; so strong was her grip that while dragging Gideon down the fateful aisle kicking, biting and screaming she must partially and irreversibly have crushed his windpipe. He can still barely talk and he always has his little notepad and pencil to hand to assist his strained gasping speech, as most folk can't understand a word he says.

Now where Val was obese and got bigger each month, Gideon was a skinny wimp with a shock of red hair. Just who was the more creepy to look at depended on which one of them had had a bath that day. Val married Gideon for the building that came with him. He was an only child and shortly after the wedding and immediately after Val had finished tampering with the brakes of his family's car, Gideon found himself a grown-up orphan with a large building on Wardour Street. A week later, Baker Productions was born; the first family of film. Val quickly gave birth to two children. Some people were surprised that Gideon had it in him, and it has been said that she dropped her sprogs the Devil's way, feet tied. Her midwife Zelda was there for both of the tummy-tearing celebrations; Zelda was never seen again after the second one.

Val never bonded with her offspring, she never gave either child her milk; secretly Val would have been found back then on the top floor breastfeeding a fully grown German shepherd that bore a remarkable resemblance to the long-lost Zelda.

Now, twenty years of wedded misery later, Val is trapped on the top floor of Wardour Street, unable to leave her garret. She is close to forty stone and on the rare occasions that she moves, she does so in slug-like fashion, unable to rise very far off the ground. A while back a doctor told her that her body was having inappropriate responses and, when she stood, instead of the blood going to her brain it would drain away causing her to faint – what a genius.

Gideon, whose shocking red hair had by this time turned brilliant white, was after all these tortuous years just as nefarious as his wicked wife. In fact, while Val thought she was in the middle of controlling the whole building via her phone and her *Minority Report* touch screen, Gideon could often be found in his own office getting off on the fact that her orders were null and void. No one had told her that her state-of-the-art hardware had never been connected to the server and so her Marcel Marceau movements were in vain, but at least they kept her arms a little more toned than the rest of her. They may even have kept her alive a little longer.

Up there on the second floor, Val's office had quickly become her home. She jokingly called it her bed and breakfast, although jocularity was never her strong point. And it was a little more than that – bed and breakfast and elevenses and lunch and a snack and then tea and then another snack and then dinner and then supper and then finally cocoa and choccy biscuits and bed, which by now was a specially made one over two metres wide. Up here could also be found Gideon's broom cupboard. He lived a little more frugally than Val.

One day, Val summoned everybody for a meeting; all the people from all the production offices nearby were coming. All the head editors, scriptwriters and casting agents, producers, directors – basically anybody to do with film – all were coming to the meeting. They had to now that Val had become too fat to leave the garret. In fact she was unable to drag herself to the other end of the room without fainting. Running would kill her, not that she would be able to lift her legs that high. As even standing up could make the blood drain from her head, she could pass out crushing anybody foolish enough to stand next to her. And if she broke wind in your direction, it could finish you off.

Val's ever suffering but strangely loyal assistant Flo read her the list of attendees. With a startling resemblance to Velma from *Scooby Doo*, Flo was bright, organised and efficient, but had a tendency to get so lost in the detail that real life seemed not to register.

Each name Flo spoke provoked a tirade of abuse from Val – abuse flowed as easily from her as an actress's tears when collecting an award – insult after insult; not once did she have a good word to say about anybody. But when they arrived later she greeted them like long-lost friends and asked them why it had been so long since they had last seen each other.

'Stephanie d'Souza,' read Flo. Now Stephanie was the most beautiful agent in Soho and cousin to an English rose who fled Somerset for Malibu. Val, the fattest, ugliest and most sweat-stained of gals, hated Stephanie more than anyone, of course. She was still a beautiful woman who could make adverts for slimming cereals and had her career ahead of her. All that Val had ahead of her was a heart attack. She grabbed the list from Flo's hand and ripped it to shreds, the veins bulging on her neck from the exertion. Nothing got her more riled than the thought of Stephanie.

'That fucking useless bitch? I remember working with her – what an experience that was! What a cunt. She expected me on location. She told me she never got my e-mails – the most pathetic and over-used excuse I hear. I nearly poisoned the bitch. God I hate her. I fucking hate her.'

Just then, walking through the door, as if on cue, comes Stephanie, Steph to all her friends, of which she has many. Sitting at the head of the table, Val regains her composure and greets Steph with apparent charm and excitement.

'Stephanie, how lovely to see you. You must pop in and see me more often. How long has it been? Let's not think about that. It will make us far too depressed.' Following this, the rest of the summoned attendees traipse reluctantly through Val's office door to begin the meeting. 'Anyway, let's get on, shall we. I've made us all tea and cakes. Let's tuck in.'

*   *   *

Gideon, whose office really was an old broom cupboard in the corner of this top floor shared with his spouse, would sit there day after day scheming and planning Val's downfall. The easiest thing would be to leave, of course, but he didn't have the courage for that and instead got comfort from daydreams of the day she would be gone and he could expand his headquarters over the entire floor.

Val had been given the news that there was no opening for her as Executive Producer on the hot new chick flick staring Sabrina Taylor and her fury was shaking the squat little building to its foundations. In a last-gasp attempt to keep her ever-hungry finger in this particular pie, she dialled Harrison Avenue to remind him of those darling images in her safe of his anus being stretched out and used by a ladyboy whore.

He laughed right back at her, telling her to feel free to go to the press. His wife found the copies sent to him and got so turned on it was like the flood before Noah set sail and she'd been fucking his ass with a strap-on ever since.

Val slammed down the phone, almost smashing it into a thousand pieces, and the anger in her face grew until her features resembled those of some hideous gargoyle – only a little bit worse.

As she begins to scream from the depths of her enormous gut, the sun disappears and the greying sky turns black with thunder; she draws her nails over the polished surface of her desk leaving jagged scars. As the rumble of thunder is followed by the first flash of lightning she wails, 'I want that film!' With all her energy, she summons up one gigantic footstep after another; it is a miracle that she doesn't fall through to the basement, floor by floor, taking all with her.

Flo, driven by her strange sense of loyalty, rushes to the aid of her mistress, but just what is in store for her she can never have imagined. Val, feeling a tingle of pleasure after ridding herself of some of the anger and stress that was in her body, knows she can get Flo to do whatever she wants. Smiling, Val says, 'Sit down, darling. There is something very special I want you to do. Get it wrong and I'll make sure that loathsome child of yours never makes it back home from that wonderful school I sent it to, ha ha ha.'

Flo whimpers, 'What can I do to help, Mrs B?'

Becoming more serious, Val tells Flo, and shortly afterwards poor Flo leaves the office to begin her assignment; she is feeling helpless and alone.

Flo is to be Baker Productions' representative at the annual Film Company Jamboree that Vinnie and James organise every year.

The team-building day dawns; the brightest staff from all the Soho film companies together with many of the owners, testament to Vinnie's powers of persuasion, are all spending the day bell-ringing at St Anne's on Wardour Street. Vinnie has lusted after the chaplain there for quite some time and is determined to get him alone today.

Flo has been primed and brainwashed but is still unsure whether she can go through with her dastardly orders. By lunchtime we know she can.

The owners of XYZ Productions who have been given Val's longed-for Exec Prod role are also a married couple, but for this town they are content and pretty normal; although known for their love of threesomes with particularly timid secretary types. Mrs XYZ is quite the butch lesbian and Mr XYZ just loves to watch. Flo lures the pair to the top of the bell tower and proceeds to feast on the wife's neatly landscaped gash just as Val had shown her. Mr Exec Producer gets behind his wife and begins to massage her tits while trying to get Flo to move on to his piece. In the frenzy that follows, during which Flo finds herself more turned on than she has ever been, she still manages to manoeuvre our happily married couple to within inches of the arched opening a hundred feet above the graveyard. Just as Mrs XYZ begins to climax, she stumbles back, helped by a gentle push from Flo, and is propelled with her husband right over the edge.

Meanwhile, on the job bringing about another climax nearby in the shadows, Vinnie emerges from beneath the chaplain's robes wondering if he is really as loud as all that, only to find himself face to face with a startled, panting, wet-mouthed Flo. She screams when she sees a vaguely familiar face and takes a step back too far, sending herself over the same edge, to the same fate. The reporter later notes that all the victims were smiling.

Vinnie, who has witnessed many scenes in his time, knows immediately this is one to cut and run from and he scarpers. The poor chaplain, still dazed from his first shared orgasm in years, drops to his knees and prays.

From her garret on Wardour Street, Val can see all through her high-powered telescope, and begins to sing in triumph. Within moments her phone rings and she is offered the role of Executive Producer on *The Snatch That Loves You*.

Elk – Waiting for the Police

The Fight that Never Happened

Soho, 1955. It was a humid August night; the only air about was coming from the mouths of all the chancers around these parts. I was meeting Betty at the coffee-bar café on Frith Street, opened a few years ago by some friends of Rocky Marciano.

I turned the corner of Old Compton and noticed how the moonlight reflected romantically off the pool of urine in the gutter. I was feeling in the mood for a little of Betty's charm that night.

There she was through the window, propped against the thin shelf on one side of the long narrow space, just lighting her cigarette. Her assisted blonde hair was shimmering under the fluorescent glow.

'Hello, sweetheart,' she cooed as I entered. This was definitely going to be the night when I would be privy to all of her womanly charms.

I took her by the waist and kissed her cheek, smelling the Chanel No. 5 that I had gotten for her just a few weeks before. Keyhole Sam had turned up at the office with a stash in his coat going cheap. I couldn't resist; it was Betty's favourite and I knew she would be putty in my hands for it.

I didn't generally deal with the Sams of this world, tried to keep on the straight and narrow, but a little knocked-off scent ain't going to hurt anyone, is it?

I lifted Betty on to a vacant red leather stool, one in a row that sprouted out of the terrazzo floor. Opposite us on the counter, the giant espresso machine hissed and fizzed as the devilishly handsome Italian boys, looking just a little sallow from being too long out of the Mediterranean sun, worked their magic with the levers and spouts to create the best coffee in town.

101

Suddenly we heard sirens, not such an unusual event in Soho; the sound became louder, then receded and stopped. It can't be too far from here I thought, always on the job.

It was getting late; Betty was looking a little tired having just finished her shift at the Café de Paris, then the hottest spot in town. The week before she had been thrilled to serve Frank Sinatra and Grace Kelly, in town to discuss with producers some new musical they were going to be doing later that year.

It was after eleven, I needed to close the deal with Betty tonight.

Just then, Little Jimmy, my young sidekick, came running in. He knew I would be in here chasing skirt.

'Quick, quick,' Jimmy cried grabbing my arm, 'you have to come now, there's been a stabbin'.'

What's the big deal I thought, these streets are full of small-time villains with knives.

'So what, kid, can't you see I'm busy?'

'No, boss, you have to come, it's Jack Spot and Italian Alberto, both of them – stabbed!'

My mood changed, those names were legend round here. Two of the most feared characters in Soho, Italian Alberto was Billy Hill's protector and Billy Hill was the boss of all bosses. Jack Spot had the penny arcade on the corner filled with one-armed bandits and delusions of grandeur. He thought he could take over Billy Hill's mantle, but we all knew that would never happen. Just another small-time crook was Jack.

I looked at Betty and then at Jimmy. I knew whom I had to follow, and it wasn't the skirt.

'Betty, doll, you understand, it's work. I gotta go, baby.'

She looked at me, rolled her eyes a little, then seemed to narrow them on the swarthy dude in the pinstripe who had been watching her from below the poster of Rocky. I could lose her this time, but it couldn't be helped.

'Jimmy, let's go.'

We sprinted out of Bar Italia, down Frith Street and round into Old Compton. Up the road, just next to the post box on the corner of Dean Street, I could see a small crowd had gathered. Off to the side was an ambulance, silent but flashing. We slowed to a casual stroll, not wishing to draw attention to ourselves, and worked our way through the gathered throng to the front.

The scene before us was bloody, the pavement glistening with the stuff. Off to the right lay Italian Alberto, handsome as a film star even now. He wasn't moving; his tightly tailored suit was shredded on his side and soaked dark red right through. His skin was pale, though his full lips were still pink.

He appeared to move slightly and groan, but it was difficult to see clearly as the two medics were working furiously pumping his chest.

Jack Spot looked in better shape. He was conscious and sitting propped against the pillar box, even managing to talk to the bobby who was bent over him, notebook in hand.

A second ambulance screamed to a halt, called, as I later found out, to the scene by the first crew. These guys weren't mugs. They knew this neighbourhood and could tell a turf-war spat when they saw one; if one or both of these guys was conscious, they needed to be kept apart.

I then noticed the first of the gangs arriving, but made sure I kept a low profile to the back of the crowd. It was Dark Irish, Billy Hill's right-hand man, along with a few of Billy's guys. They were eyeballing the scene, but didn't move in too close and couldn't have known if Alberto was alive or dead.

Dark Irish was small and tightly muscled, with bony features, pale skin, even paler blue eyes and thick black hair, heavily greased into a DA. He had a permanent five o'clock shadow and was always puffing heavily on his untipped Players.

I knew Billy Hill could not be far away, although he would never show his face with all this going on. He would be round the corner sitting in the back of his Wolseley. Billy was the guv'nor of Soho, king of the hill. A gentleman gangster who always made sure that his turf was clean. No drugs with Billy, the prostitutes were safe, and to the little old ladies who lived in these streets he was a saint. Always immaculate in his Savile Row suits, he was quite the charmer. Of course all that charm couldn't fully disguise the psychopathic dealings that were part of the job description. He was not a man to cross.

I felt a tap on my shoulder and turned: it was Eddie, one of my snitches.

'I saw it all, fellas. You wanna know what happened? Got a ciggie, Little Jimmy? I could murder a drink.'

I reached into my jacket pocket and retrieved my flask of whisky. I handed it to Eddie to grease his tongue. He took a swig, revealing his rotten yellow teeth; I caught a whiff of his acrid breath and turned my head slightly. He offered the flask back; I told him to keep it and to start walking with us while he talked.

We moved away from the scene of the crime, and what with the whisky and the guinea that I gave him, Eddie began spilling the beans, no problem. We headed towards Soho Square where we could take a pew in the dark and talk without being overheard.

Eddie revealed what had happened before the carnage. Italian Alberto had been sauntering up Old Compton Street happy as a lark. He had spent his usual Tuesday night at White City and all his tips had come in. He was puffed up with success, even bunging Eddie a cigar and a note while telling him of his successful night at the dogs. He had looked particularly handsome that evening; the local girls were all wondering if one of them would be lucky enough to be his date for that night. Alberto was on top of the world just then.

He had walked along Frith Street past Jack Spot's arcade before turning into Old Compton Street, and Eddie had noticed Jack come out the door and follow Alberto, catching up with him just as he got to the corner of Dean Street. Jack shouted, 'Alberto,' and stretched out his arm as if to shake hands. Instead of doing this though he had quickly pulled back his hand and snatched a knife from beneath his jacket, stabbing Alberto in his side three or four times, quick as a flash. Alberto had staggered back a few steps, but had kept his balance, even managing to pull out the knife embedded in his side. Eddie described him as like Victor Mature in *Samson and Delilah*. He had plunged it straight back into Jack, just missing his jugular, a bull's eye which would have killed him on the spot. Instead the knife entered his shoulder with such force that Jack was the first to fall to the ground.

Alberto kept his composure and managed to sit himself down on the kerb. Almost immediately, however, he had passed out and slumped back, his head hitting the pavement.

'Is there anything else you're not telling, Eddie?' I felt sure he was holding something back.

'No, nothing, big man, nothing. Gotta go,' and with that he was off, scurrying into the night, the cap of my hip flask still twinkling in his hand.

Hearing the tinny ring of ambulance bells brought me back to reality. Jimmy and I without speaking hurried back toward the scene of the crime. This kid was good, would go places for sure.

A small crowd still lingered on the corner; a couple of despondent-looking boys in blue were trying to get info from some of the bystanders, but the only response they appeared to be getting was a slow shake of the head as the folk dispersed.

I noticed Frank, a new young recruit to the local force, ambitious and eager to stamp his mark on Soho's streets. I caught his eye.

'So what's the story, Frankie?' He was fresh-faced, recently shaved with a spot of dried blood on his nicked chin. His uniform was immaculately pressed, his shoes so shiny I was tempted to take out my comb.

'Can't say and no one's talking. At least they had the sense to take 'em to separate hospitals. The Italian's gone to St George's, Jack the lad has been taken to St Thomas's.'

I nodded and motioned to Jimmy as the copper walked off. I told the kid to leg it down to Lambeth and find out what was happening to Jack. I headed off toward the park and Italian Alberto's destination.

*　　*　　*

When I awoke very early the next day the hazy sunshine was already streaming through the thin drapes that barely covered my window. Summer was crazy – the darkness only fleeting. I had a headache. Getting up, I made coffee and lit my first cigarette of the day. I sat down at the table, and pushing a pile of books out of my way, I opened my notebook and started to go over last night's events.

Italian Alberto had been taken to surgery; he was still alive but it was touch-and-go. Hooked up to a drip in a side room, he had half the force posted outside his door.

Jack Spot, once the knife was removed and a few stitches were inserted, had been picked up by some of his guys planning to take him home to Camden Town. Jimmy, who had been sitting on my front step when I got back, told me that as Jack left the hospital building, supported by two of his cronies, the Old Bill swooped from their Jags and arrested him. The Black Maria had come screaming round the corner and Jack was off to Bow Street Station.

I knew Jimmy would be back soon, keen to continue our investigation. I put on a pot of water so I could shave. When he arrived we headed off to see what had become of Italian Alberto.

As it transpired, he had come round during the night, a fighter all right. And now fully conscious, he was handcuffed to his bed and saying nothing, according to the pretty little nurse we sweet-talked outside. We hung around for a while longer, looking for the scoop, but left unenlightened for Frith Street, a decent coffee and some local gossip after an hour or so.

Bar Italia was abuzz – stabbings might not have been so unusual in Soho, but this one was different. It could alter these streets for ever, could mean a change in the order of things around these parts.

For the next few weeks Soho was on tenterhooks. People were edgy. Jack Spot who had been released twenty-four hours after his arrest was nowhere to be seen, lying low; terrified, I'm sure, of repercussions. The arcade was closed until further notice.

Italian Alberto had been released from hospital and custody a few weeks after the stabbing and was convalescing down Margate way, so we heard.

We never saw Billy Hill around either, although he still was running our little village from his town house off Shepherd Market.

By the time the leaves started falling in late October, the trial was set.

On the first day, I found myself jostled in the crowd outside the Old Bailey; the hacks were out in force, and the rubberneckers were behaving as if they were at a big fight. As each car drew up and disgorged its occupants they cheered or booed. I knew whom I was cheering for. Diana Dors even put in an appearance; rumour had it she'd been taking a little of Margate's sea air.

I managed to squeeze my way into the public gallery; the atmosphere was electric, it could have been the première of Stewart Granger's new picture.

Italian Alberto stood in the dock on one side looking more handsome than ever. With his hair cut shorter than usual, he was a dead ringer for Marlon Brando.

Jack Spot looked gaunt in the dock on the opposite side; his suit had been taken in a few inches. Obviously he had not had such a good time these past couple of months.

The clerk shouted, 'All rise,' as the judge, Mr Justice Stoppard, took his pew, bringing order to the occasion with a slam of his gavel.

I studied the jury. They were all dressed to the nines in their Sunday best, new togs one and all by the looks of things, probably living rent-free now. I turned and looked again at Alberto: he seemed relaxed and I think I even saw him wink toward the beehive of the blonde sitting down below me.

And so it began.

A week later we were back on the steps outside; the court had been cleared while the jury came back. The judge had decreed that they would be heard behind closed doors. We all stood silent, waiting to hear the news. Tonight could be very bloody in Soho if things didn't turn out right. A small man in a short black cape came running out through the heavy oak doors.

'No verdict, case dismissed, no retrial!' he shouted, the last syllable almost drowned out by the collective roar. The relief was intense; the residents of Soho would sleep well that night, now the old order was restored. It was the fight that never happened.

*   *   *

EPILOGUE

The arcade is under new management. I'm back collecting thrup'n'y fines on late returns at Charing Cross Library. Supposed to be meeting Betty at Bar Italia this evening, she's got the night off; fingers crossed no interruptions.

Jim Lambie – Soho Rox

The Prince of Soho

It all began in Kensington almost two decades ago, just a whisper away from the Palace. Rather fitting for the birth of a prince.

In those days it was a place of small independent boutiques, not the clothing chains and computer megastores of today. Nestling among the designer labels was a little bureau de change, part of the business empire of money man Des and his merry men; here they cashed cheques for the rich, offered commission-free currency to the poorer and overpriced balcony seats to the tourists.

It had all started when the owner of this little booth had wished to expand his business. Des, with his untraceable cash, had come to the rescue, mesmerising the owner with tales of wheeling and dodgy dealing in South London. An office was spawned in a nearby office block and the booth became the domain of Des's nephew, Vinnie. A rather forgettable little guy in those days, who kept his head down and got on with the job with an odd combination of bravado and timidity, he was being moulded by his family to be something he never wanted to be.

He longed to escape from behind that little stable door with the counter on top. In time he began to share his dreams with the designers and wannabe models from boutiques next to the shop and soon became firm friends with all of them. So, on the day when hard man Des slapped him across the face because of some missing tickets that Des had in his pocket all along, Vinnie's new friends closed ranks. One offered a place to stay, another a job and another offered the most helpful advice of all: 'Just because they are your own flesh and blood, it doesn't mean you owe them anything. You are your own person; you need to get away, create your own life, your own family, your own destiny.' This was James – Joe Buck to Vinnie's Ratso or Brad to Vinnie's Angelina, Vinnie thought in his more fanciful moments.

Vinnie slowly began to come out of his shell. He quit his job and found himself a few stand-in shifts at Hyper-Hyper. That led to him being asked to run the café at a low-rent version of it in the King's Road. The place had no natural light and a terrible stench; Vinnie soon began to wither and knew he had to move on. He went just next door to Chelsea Town Hall, working for the caterers there, a pair of bent ex-coppers. Vinnie, who was still a product of his crooked past, knew that as they were so busy covering their own tracks from the bookkeeper, they would not have the time to be checking his. Open season at the town hall meant a flurry of transferred bills, managed with a skill he had never lost but which had, like a fine wine, matured.

But that could never last and soon he told James he had to move on, and, bearing in mind his words of wisdom, was taking the number 19 bus up to the West End – Piccadilly, in fact – in search of a job at some soon-to-open palace of pleasure.

He went, he met, he conquered; the owners were smitten; it helped that they were smacked out at the time.

And so it really began. The roller-coaster ride that was the Pacific Bar and Grill was the real start of the rise of our prince. Here was where Vinnie's star began to shine. Here he first met Sonny, one of the many loves of his life, and had his first insight into just how ruthless these places and people could be.

On opening night, Marcia and Donna, the girls on reception, were strutting their stuff. Well known on the concierge scene, these were girls who knew their way around. They understood how it worked: dealers turn up at these new spots all the time, scouting for business, giving the good-looking chicks on the desk freebies; before you know it these girls are dealing to customers and a business relationship has been born. Now these girls were already in with their dealers, so no schmoozing was required, and on this, the opening night, they had a kilo to hold. It might seem like a lot, but believe me, it's very necessary to supply the demand if any bar is to take serious amounts of cash. The economics are simple: bar without supply – five grand take; with supply – fifteen.

The girls were enjoying the buzz. As anyone can tell you, reception areas, because of their very nature, are central to any establishment. As first point of contact with the outside world they are notoriously corrupt places and in any establishment, no matter how refined and lofty, there is no escape from the dodgy goings-on of the concierge. The people who run them have a high status within the workforce and can always sort something or somebody out.

However, at a certain moment on that opening night, Marcia and Donna suddenly realised they had misplaced the entire kilo of coke and their buzz turned to worry and then blind panic, they had lost it for sure. At the end of the evening they had to own up, and as you can imagine it did not go down well. But drug dealers are rarely violent in public, it's bad for business, and in this case a pact was agreed so that these two young women would be used as whores by whoever the dealer might send to them. Any day, any night, sometimes one, sometimes ten men would turn up and use a codeword. On hearing this either Donna or Marcia would have to take them back into the cavernous room that acted as cloakroom and get them off in whatever way was required. There was no time limit to this pay back, it only ended when Donna left for Hawaii and Marcia ran off screaming into the night almost a year later. One time they even gave away a freebie: some totally random and unconnected guy turned up at the desk and said something to Marcia, who, thinking she had heard that damn word, duly took his hand, led him into the back and gave him a very unexpected start to his night.

After a year or so, Vinnie's drug debts were so large he had to take extra work at the newest mega-bistro in town. The day he realised his debts were repaid he left mid-shift and has never been back.

However, he was still drowning in narcotics at this point. One night, his friend James found him slumped at the door of the pleasure palace after his shift, waiting to go out. Dressed from the neck down in fluorescent orange Lycra, he seemed confused and was visibly drooling. Vinnie's response to James's questioning came too late for James to hear as he turned and walked away from the somnolent figure. 'I'm supposed to be a disco tangerine, please don't leave me,' he had begged James's distant shadow.

A few days later, while hurtling around Russell Square in his GTI Mk1, James had told Vinnie, now slumped in his passenger seat, that he had lost all the charm he once had. James offered him shelter in Bloomsbury, a quiet place to dry out. Vinnie jumped at the chance, having not slept in weeks and feeling just a little ashamed of himself as a disco tangerine. He turned up at the door, bag in hand, later that night.

Vinnie slept for two days straight, but on the third night he received a phone call. 'I have to go meet someone just around the corner to get something,' he said.

'Tell them to come round here,' James replied.

'No, no, I'll be back in five minutes,' cried Vin.

He rang James's bell three days later wearing someone else's clothes. It was then Vinnie finally accepted things had to change; after a fashion and after a while they did.

Without James, there would have been no prince, just an ugly drug-fucked old toad.

He began to do more shifts at the Flamingo, leaving the Pacific for ever when Dick took him to the Groucho Club, his first trip to that particular joint. Here they were looking for wait staff to fill out the rota. Vinnie was game and desperate for work a little less dangerous to his health, and so a legend was born.

On his first shift he arrived at reception to be greeted by a rather vulgar but gregarious bald man with jazz hands – that was Andy.

He was scheduled for shifts in the brasserie or dining-room, downstairs or up.

In those days the place was a little smarter, more formal and still fresh with the stamp of professional and not amateur decorating. There was navy-blue felt on the walls and matching carpet.

Vinnie was sent to the dining-room, the club's own little piece of Siberia; it has always been slightly chilly in there – never the best resolved space in this place. No one has ever figured out quite how to deal with the lovely arched and glazed roof in a way that will warm the interior up. It was no help that straight through the old fire exit was something of a roof terrace, an outdoor space squashed between buildings and destined to make the perfect smoking terrace.

Running the restaurant with a rod of iron was Michelle from Australia. She placed him by the table and showed him how the cutlery should be laid out, telling him that if it was not done every time in this way his failure would be classed as insubordination and he would be fined out of his tips. He didn't bother to tell her that he had learnt his craft at the Savoy when she was still playing in dust near Mount Isa.

'We always practise the five p's,' she had chanted. ' "Prior preparation prevents poor performance." ' Vinnie loved that line, and has used it ever since. At the time her charms were hardly apparent and Vinnie had marched straight up to his friend Chris, the bar manager, asking if the outback bitch was for real.

Promptly summoned to see Jytte in the brasserie, Vinnie was struck by its total contrast to the dining-room; this space was always warm, the lighting was good and it had a beautiful marble floor (no longer on show but covered by a carpet these days to deaden the echo); he always thought that brasseries were supposed to be a little noisy and bustling.

Jytte proceeded to tell him that she knew he had been gossiping about her and spreading rumours and why would he do such a thing? He had looked at her in total confusion, but it quickly dawned on him that he was working in a mad house. He mentioned the fact that having been there all of ten minutes, he knew nothing about her and was still trying to learn his five p's. With that she slammed her fist on the table and told him never to interrupt her or gossip about her again. He had had his warning. Never was that first meeting mentioned again and never did Vinnie interrupt Jytte. Now, sent back upstairs, he encountered a Bionic-Woman-lookalike hanging pictures; it was Nicky, the club's art curator and the most straightforward person he has met in that place to date.

'Oh hi, you must be Vinnie? Dick and Chris told me to look out for you. Are you having a nice time? It can be a lot of fun here, although they are a little cranky in the daytime and I decided a long time ago never to work on a Monday.' She smiled. 'Good luck, have fun.'

This charming interaction was interrupted by mistress-five-p shouting down from the top of the stairs that he was not there to socialise and would be promptly fined his first week's tips. Such was his welcome to this particular lunatic asylum.

What he was later to learn, unsurprisingly, was that the five head waiters were something of a cabal, and kept all the new waiters' tips by fining them; it paid for their fun and games; it was usually months before you saw any tronc.

He did take Nicky's advice though, and avoided the day shifts from then on as much as he could; they were edgy at best, you just had to keep a low profile and get on with it. 'Never make any decisions until the moon has replaced the sun,' became a rule he still lives by.

He worked in that restaurant for the best part of a year before moving to the bar, a better gig, people being easier to deal with when drunk than hungry – usually.

Not the naturally competitive type who excels at bar waiting, he could be quite oblivious to people's needs. One evening, while spinning through a shift, Vinnie was stopped by another waiter wanting to know where some guy's coffee was. 'Coffee?' he'd replied. 'What coffee?'

'That guy wants a cappuccino,' his colleague had said, pointing at some cranky member.

'Oh, I thought he told me I looked like Al Pacino,' Vinnie replied. 'No wonder he looked confused when I said thank you in response.'

If memory served him right that same waiter got the guy's coffee double quick. Remember a good tip can often be had if you sort out someone's problem.

After a long stretch at the bar – years, Vin needed to get out. Nothing had changed there and he needed to sing a new song, or was that have a vodka and slimline. He put on some Ron Hills, bought some new trainers, grew his hair and attended the YMCA, where he got his qualification in teaching disco dancing to senior citizens. Not bad for someone who left school at twelve.

There is even a video somewhere James made of Vinnie holding a class on the roof of the Oasis, filmed when they were trying to turn him into Britain's answer to Richard Simmons.

What fun that day had been and the video isn't half bad. In it were Vinnie's fan base, average age sixty-five. There was the crazy old artist and Rhoda, his mother; there was Stan and his tremendous cock that Vinnie was obsessed with – no matter how hard he tried, he always found himself staring at Stan's semi in the changing room – he would have sucked that seventy-five-year-old dry and is proud to admit it.

Not long after a doomed love affair that he quickly recovered from, despite thinking he never would, he received a phone call from the Groucho saying they needed a receptionist. As he'd never done that particular gig, and had only one remaining client alive, the offer was tempting, so he waited until evening and then phoned the iconic June and told her she was on. And it was thus he returned, his hair newly flowing, wearing his white Pierre Cardin slip-ons. As he stood at the desk to welcome back his crowd, each and every one, juggling their needs and charming the pants off them, promising to fix whatever needed fixing, all in a whirl of gestures, hugs and kisses, Stephen Fry interrupted the love-in by placing a gentle hand under Vinnie's chin and breathing the words: 'Darling boy, you clearly are the Prince of Soho.'

Vinnie thought about this later; it was a role he had never envisaged for himself. It had been quite a long slog: from waiter through barman and club host to number-one club host at Soho central. Perhaps this longevity was truly the reason for his crown. Being central to this distorted vision of village life, knowing everyone who ever ran as much as a tap in these hallowed streets, that gives you an in. And then there's the showbiz crowd, he knows them as well, the producers, the directors, the editors. And the most slippery of all, the casting agents, whose lives are devoted to changing the goal posts and the time of your meeting – just to keep you on your toes. Then there are the gangsters; to this day they are everywhere around these parts and you definitely need to know how to play their game if you want to survive and prosper round here, and Vinnie was born to that, knows them better than they know themselves. And then there are the locals, that colourful posse. From Phil, seven feet tall in his bowler, who threw the best parties ever, to Blair, who has worked at just about every restaurant and club in Soho, filling the gaps in her split-shifted days by turning tricks at the knocking shop on the corner. She is barely five feet tall in her heels, with wonderful blonde hair. She has worked these rather full days for as long as Vinnie can remember. So next time you're eating out in one of Soho's many watering holes, remember your waitress could very well be Blair; watch out for the side orders, she's great at those!

Turning up to all the parties throughout the year and being seen in all the right places; at the end of the night, more often than not, screaming out, 'Rowie, I adore you' – although Rowie's days are numbered now Sam is about; riding the red carpet arm in arm with the latest star in town; climbing through the windows of a production company with Sabrina Taylor just to have a fag inside and not out – which must surely be non-PC; all of these contributing factors explain how Vinnie became the Prince of Soho. He has a talent for turning up in two places at once in different outfits. He always has a story to tell with his razor-sharp wit. His life is crazy, but he flows through it with ease and the occasional Valium. When being asked by a handsome man on karaoke night what song he will sing, his quick reply is always 'You're The One That I Want'. And just as the handsome man smiles, his wife will appear to drag him away while freezing out poor Vinnie with her evil eye.

Some hotshot producer guy once took Vinnie out to dinner at Le Caprice, promising him stardom, fame and fortune. Hip to these men and their propositions, Vinnie had only gone as he was ravenous and he had not seen the Caprice boys in ages; he thought he could kill two birds with one rock.

'Thanks, honeysuckle,' came Vinnie's reply when the offer was made, 'I just think that I would make a dreadful actor. Well, I'd want to be in every scene for a start.' He stopped talking and just munched his way through the rest of the evening. The next day at work Vinnie received a bouquet of black orchids wrapped in barbed wire, sent by the enraged producer's wife. Lauren turned and asked why she had sent this to him. Does she want you to keep away? she had wondered dramatically. Vinnie shrugged his shoulders. 'Maybe she was hungry and I ate her dinner.' Vinnie never saw him again.

It could also be down to the fact that he tries to keep the memory of Dirtbox alive by hosting a seasonal disco four times a year, getting the old gang back together, with Sonny on the decks pumping out the unforgettable classics. And they will all pitch up, well those that are still with us, and for those that are not, he lays flowers. Dear Lisa, we will always follow your total eclipse.

*   *   *

There are so many reasons why Vinnie is the Prince of Soho. But in the last analysis, through all the fiascos and the dramas, some way too hot to print and better left unsaid, tales that would probably make you feel sick, there is the kiss.

It's in his kiss – he has kissed the whole of Soho one way or another, there is nobody else like him and there never will be again – thank you, God. One random day, a club member was in Los Angeles playing poker in a tent with five other guys; as way of a story he mentioned the shabby old club back in London where he had been just two nights before. He laughed as he told his chums about drunkenly kissing Vinnie hard and passionately when he left. One by one, the other men around the table, all married of course, replied with their own tale of kissing our prince, the last one topping them all by telling his tale of having sex with Vinnie. How they had all laughed. All this in LA in a tent – wait till Vinnie gets there himself; look out LA!

Last night, at the end of another long and exhausting carouse on those rat-infested streets that we love, a group of young vampires wanting more bloody marys stopped Vinnie while he was dashing for his ride. 'Where's the best place to go now?' they had cried. Vinnie crossed the road, giving them his best cat-walk strut, struck a pose and replied simply: 'Home.'

Pissed Soho Women of Certain Years

Pissed Soho women of certain years, sucking on face tubes 'til their inside cheeks are touching and their ears move back an inch. Wanting to be rude, but without the ammunition, downturned bitter lips and eyelids fishing fishing fishing, not for compliments but for confidence and shampoo, time flies when you're looking back at life from the bottom of a champagne flute. But when the bottles bottoms up in the bucket and all the bubbles have popped in the pit of your twisted stomach, and a bubbly twenty something, pert and cute, is perched at the bar with a pinstripe suit and a split up her skirt with a handful of loot. And that's when your personal party exits through the back door and someone else has sneaked in through the side door and they've brought a few friends along to join the fun and glee. They brought spiteful, nasty and greedy to name but three then they fall off their stools and put their coats on upside down and inside out so their collars are hanging round their arses and they're falling all about then they spit fuck off! to all in the room fall up the stairs and before too soon they're spilling their bile in Old Compton Street. Get as far as Camisa's and they fall in a heap and they wake up in a cell in the morning. You know the type. Well I've got quite a soft spot for them.

Phil Dirtbox

PISSED SOHO WOMEN OF CERTAIN YEARS.

PISSED SOHO WOMEN OF CERTAIN YEARS,
SUCKING ON FACE TUBES 'TIL THEIR INSIDE CHEEKS
ARE TOUCHING. ~~WANTING TO BE~~ RUDE, BUT
~~WITHOUT THE AMMUNITION~~ AND THEIR EARS
MOVE BACK AN INCH. WANTING TO BE RUDE, BUT WITHOUT
THE ~~AMM~~UNITION, DOWNTURNED BITTER LIPS + EYELIDS
FISHING FISHING FISHING, NOT FOR COMPLIMENTS
BUT FOR CONFIDENCE AND SHAMPOO, TIME FLYS
WHEN YOU'RE LOOKING BACK ~~AT LIFE~~ FROM THE
BOTTOM OF A CHAMPAGNE FLUTE. AND A BUBBLY
TWENTY SOMETHING, PERT + CUTE, IS PERCHED AT
THE BAR WITH A ~~HANDFULL OF LOOT~~ PINSTRIPE
SUIT AND A SPLIT UP HER SKIRT WITH A HANDFULL
OF LOOT. AND THAT'S WHEN YOUR PERSONAL
PARTY EXITS THROUGH THE BACK DOOR AND SOMEONE
ELSE HAS SNEAKED IN THROUGH THE SIDE DOOR
AND THEY'VE BROUGHT A FEW FRIENDS ALONG
TO JOIN THE FUN + GLEE. THEY BROUGHT
~~SPITEFULL~~, NASTY + GREEDY TO NAME BUT 3
THEN THEY FALL OFF THEIR STOOLS AND PUT
THEIR COATS ON UPSIDE DOWN AND INSIDE OUT
~~THEN THEY SPIT FUCK OFF! TO ALL IN THE ROOM~~
~~AND THEY'RE FALLING ALL ABOUT THEN THEY FALL~~
~~UP THE~~ SO THEIR COLLARS ARE HANGING ROUND
THEIR ARSES AND THEY'RE FALLING ALL ABOUT
THEN THEY SPIT FUCK OFF! TO ALL IN THE ROOM
FALL UP THE STAIRS AND BEFORE TOO SOON
THEY'RE SPILLING THEIR BILE IN OLD COMPTON
ST. GET AS FAR AS CAMISA'S AND THEY FALL
IN A HEAP AND THEY WAKE UP IN A CELL
IN THE MORNING. YOU KNOW THE TYPE,
WELL I'VE GOT QUITE A SOFT SPOT FOR THEM

INSERT:

BUT WHEN THE BOTTLES BOTTOMS UP IN THE BUCKET AND ALL THE BUBBLES HAVE POPPED IN THE PIT OF YOUR TWISTED STOMACH

Date

Signature

Print Name

Tony Husband – Chasing Artists

Acknowledgements

Most of all, my thanks are to Soho, for teaching me all its tricks so well. This book is for you. I hope the stories have brought a smile to your face and at times wiped it clean away . . . most of all I hope it has given you an insight into this infuriating little village that we all love and that we call home.

There are so many people to thank for making possible these stories. First and foremost is Rosemary Reed, who thought ten years ago I had something but could never quite put her finger on it. One night not so long ago, I was ranting about Lord knows what (Mars must have been in my moon that day and had a fight) and Rosemary came up to me and said, 'Sweet child of God, what passion. You should write that down' . . . well, here it is ! Without your help and belief, this twisted love story would never have been told. Without Rosemary Reed I would still be shouting at the banisters. What a truly wonderful lady she is.

Then there is Caroline de Wolfe, an angel. One day alone I swear I called her a hundred and fifty times and each time she answered with her soothing tone. She always managed to make the most awful of deadlines and strictest of instructions sound like a stroll down Bond Street to go shopping at LV for a new customised Gladstone bag. Once Caroline's voice was but a memory, the realisation would hit. Not only were you not going to Bond Street, and not getting your beloved bag, but instead you had been given a sharp reminder that you had just three hours to hand in four completed stories. But how lovely she is . . . and would be even lovelier if she ever got around to taking me to Bond Street . . .

What can I say about Stephen Fry that hasn't been said before? A truly great man, a god for our times. It's an opinion I have heard expressed time after time by admirers, from a lady to a noble man, an actress or comedian to the world's greatest graffiti artist, and even by my niece, for whom Stephen once wrote a poem. Oh how she danced around the room when I gave it to her! What words can even touch on what it means to me to have him write such a tender foreward and for him to be so connected with all of these pages. Dear, dear Stephen, please be patient with me as I still can't find any words that suffice. I think I'll just have to give you the biggest kiss there is on our next encounter. And I'm sure that's just around the corner. Beware of corners, Mr Fry; my lips are puckering in your direction.

Then there is Richard Bacon, the godfather of the Friday fun club. It's going to get so busy that it will need its own secretary soon. Perhaps Fiona, and Kirsty can head up debates . . . Then there's Richard's beautiful wife Rebecca, who single-handedly stopped me being marched off to the cop shop. Anything you want, you can have.

To Grant Nivison, or James if you prefer, go eternal thanks. Without this amazing man who has put up with and looked out for me for over twenty years, I would be dead, and this book would never have happened. I couldn't have done it without you, honey cherub. You made this possible. Who would have thought when I tried to flog you knocked-off leggings all those years ago that this is where we would end up? Finally one of our crazy ideas paid off. Thank God I got out of Lycra. I know he wants to dedicate his part to his parents, Nadine and Tom. Oh how I loved her jewels ! And to Chris for his love and support . . . where's my Obsession?

Danny Wallace, an enormous thank-you for all your help, especially for the polish to my biog.

To Piers, for being so patient and putting up with our overrun deadlines and the ever-changing acknowledgements; but there were so many people to thank . . . and I thank you.

Thank you also to Elk. May every spray can and paintbrush be held up to the sky in your honour (you know not what Voodoo you do).

Mode 2, Elk is under the moon with open arms shouting, 'Amazing.'

Thank you, Phil Dirtbox. No book about Soho could be about Soho without your wise words.

A special thank you to the lovely Ben Oliver for introducing us to Minho Kwon.

Thank you to Remi of Greek Street for helping me reel in the artwork.

Well done Paul Cassidy (South London man, done superb).

A huge thanks to Jessica Adams for her help on the biogs.

To all of Soho's members' clubs, especially the Union where many hours of writing took place in the daytime and many coffees were nursed. I know I drove you all mad with my unrealistic demands. What can I say? I want it now! – WHERE IS IT?

A special thank-you to Mary-Lou Sturridge, co-founder StreetSmart.

Love and thanks to the Prince of Soho's gang – all clued up but clueless (thanks Jeanne): Katie McGuiness, June McCluskey, Kent Olesen, Sophy Smith, Amy, Monica, Kate P and Rachel. Lucy, Alton and Claire from Black's. Michael Smith and Alistair. Michael Law and Lilly Barker.

To Triana Terry, the only girl I know that can paint the Sistine Chapel on a piece of A4.

Ian Sanderson, we languish in other people's beds and watch telly – Who will be Nancy? We never found out. We didn't care.

To my mother Rhoda Katz, star of the infamous fitness video *Disco Dancing for Senior Citizens*, which I made with Grant many years ago when he was trying to turn me into England's answer to Richard Simmons – how they ran for their lives!

My sisters, Karon, Debbie and Lesley.

And to my Blackheath family, Sarah and Rita Lehane.

And finally to the following, extraordinary artists, whose contribution has made this book totally unique. I am so proud to be immortalised with you all in these pages – Sir Peter Blake, Elk, Tracey Emin, Nina Fowler, Damien Hirst, Carl Hopgood, Rachel Howard, Tony Husband, Minho Kwon, Jim Lambie, Sarah Lucas, John Maybury, Tim Noble, Marc Quinn, Sam Taylor-Wood, Triana de Lamo Terry, Sue Webster and Jonathan Yeo.

I thank all of you. Thank you, thank you, thank you . . .

Bernie

Damien Hirst – Soho

BIOGRAPHIES

SARAH LUCAS

Sarah Lucas was born in Holloway, London, in 1962 and studied at Goldsmiths' College. She was included in the ground-breaking group exhibition Freeze in 1988 with contemporaries including Angus Fairhurst, Damien Hirst and Gary Hume.

Since her first two solo exhibitions in 1992, presciently titled The Whole Joke and Penis Nailed to a Board, Lucas has continued to appropriate everyday materials to make works that use humour, visual puns and sexual metaphor to discuss sex, death, Englishness and gender.

Her work has been included in most major surveys of new British art in the last decade, including Sensation – Young British Artists from the Saatchi Collection at the Royal Academy (1997) and Brooklyn Museum (1998) and Intelligence – New British Art 2000 at Tate Britain. Lucas has had solo exhibitions at Boymans-van Beuningen Museum in Rotterdam (1996), the Ludwig Museum in Cologne (1997) and the Freud Museum in London (2002), and a major one-person-survey show at Kunsthalle Zurich and Tate Liverpool in 2005, for which a *catalogue raisonné* was published.

Sarah Lucas lives and works in London and is represented by Sadie Coles HQ.

TRIANA DE LAMO TERRY

Triana de Lamo Terry was born in Central London on 2 December 1985. She began painting with oils in her final years at Eastbourne College before going on to drama school and graduating in 2008. Her father, Richard Terry, also an artist, owned a commercial-art studio in Soho. Soho has been very much part of her life. She has a Spanish mother, Celia de Lamo, who is a photojournalist and documentary-film maker. Triana has been influenced by early works of the Pre-Raphaelites and also contemporary artist Paula Rego in the strength of her character portrayal.

MARC QUINN

Marc Quinn's wide-ranging *oeuvre* displays a preoccupation with the mutability of the body and the dualisms that define human life: spiritual and physical, surface and depth, cerebral and sexual. Using an uncompromising array of materials, from ice and blood to glass, marble and lead, Quinn develops these paradoxes into experimental, conceptual works that are mostly figurative in form.

Quinn's sculptures, paintings and drawings often deal with the distanced relationship we have with our bodies, highlighting how the conflict between the 'natural' and 'cultural' has a grip on the contemporary psyche. In 1999, Quinn began a series of marble sculptures of amputees as a way of rereading the aspirations of Greek and Roman statuary and their depictions of an idealised whole. One such work took as its subject Alison Lapper, a woman who was born without arms, when she was heavily pregnant. Quinn subsequently enlarged this work to make it a major piece of public art for the fourth plinth in Trafalgar Square. Other key themes in his work include genetic modification and hybridism. *Garden* (2000), for instance, is a walk-through installation of impossibly beautiful flowers that will never decay, and his 'Eternal Spring' sculptures feature flowers preserved in perfect bloom by being plunged into sub-zero silicone. Quinn has also explored the potential artistic uses of DNA, making a portrait of a sitter by extracting strands of DNA and placing them in a test-tube. *DNA Garden* (2001) contains the DNA of over seventy-five plant species and two humans: a re-enactment of the Garden of Eden on a cellular level. Quinn's diverse and poetic work meditates on our attempts to understand or overcome the transience of human life through scientific knowledge and artistic expression.

Marc Quinn has exhibited in many important group and solo exhibitions internationally, including Sonsbeek '93, Arnhem (1993), Give and Take, Victoria and Albert Museum, London (2001), Statements 7, 50th Venice Biennale (2003) and Gwangju Biennale (2004). Solo exhibitions include Tate Gallery, London (1995), Kunstverein Hannover (1999), Fondazione Prada, Milan (2000), Tate Liverpool (2002), Irish Museum of Modern Art, Dublin (2004), Groninger Museum, Groningen (2006) and MACRO, Rome (2006).

NINA FOWLER

Nina's work offers a gentle glance at the gap between idolisation and the idolised. Using pencil to create a highly detailed image – almost photographic in its quality – Nina plays on the gap between fantasy and reality, the screen idol made material, bought closer through the humble medium of pencil. This image of Brando is taken from his 1953 portrayal of Mark Antony, archetypal hero and proud soldier, and his gold-leafed armour exudes a certain valour and embellished masculinity. The shining armour and hero's pose, however, thinly disguise the vulnerability of the man beneath, another comment on the gap between portrayal and truth, the depiction of the actor as screen-god and the reality of the man behind the image. The frame, sculpted and cast in resin/plaster, is constructed of a series of adoring, subserviant women, all in various states of blind agony. Clearly, Nina has referenced classical Greek and Roman sculpture, as well as its interpretation by later figures such as Bernini and Rodin. However, these women are not entirely submissive nineteenth-century constructs for they represent a little discussed twenty-first-century post-feminism construct – the woman who chooses for her own reasons, in her own time, to submit to inner desires of subservience and idolisation. The crux of so much of her work is here portrayed in a way that pretends to be nothing more than a retrograde rear-view of the idolised – the irony, or lack of it, is entirely dependent on the predisposition of the viewer.

Nina was born in London in 1981 and graduated from Brighton University in 2003 with a degree in sculpture. Since then she has been developing a body of work exploring the interdisciplinary potential of working across the mediums of fine art. Her practice engages traditional methods of printmaking, drawing, sculpture and photography, all of which are combined to challenge and complement one another.

The underlying theme, which runs throughout the work, is desire – sometimes simply in the form of the impossible yearnings that exist between the icon and the fanatic, sometimes in the form of a challenge to her viewer to question more deeply the intense self-deceptive seduction of our idols.

Nina has recently started exhibiting in London after working principally on private commissions. Recent group shows include Don't Stop Me Now – The Body Beyond Death, Trolley Gallery (2008) and the BP Portrait Award 2008 at the National Portrait Gallery. She has work on permanent display at the Colony Room Club in London and currently works as assistant and archivist to John Dunbar (former owner of the Indica Gallery). She has a forthcoming solo show in 2009 and continues to undertake private commissions.

CARL HOPGOOD

British artist Carl Hopgood is one of the most exciting and experimental of his generation. Working in film, sculpture, photography and sound, he combines these media to create some of the most beautiful and unique *trompe-l'oeil* art-works. He creates a timeless celluloid world that we can only dream of being a part of. Sharing his voyeuristic private world is an experience often sad, always beautiful, sometimes uncomfortable.

Born in Wales on a farm, Carl moved to London in the early 1990s to study art at Goldsmiths' College. The heady nightclubs and prevailing party scene of Soho were very seductive to a Welsh boy from the countryside.

Gaining a first-class honours degree, Carl was immediately offered a solo show at not just one but two major London galleries. The critically acclaimed show, titled Arrivals Departures, exhibited a style of work that had never been seen before.

Some of Carl's work is on permanent show at the Groucho Club and he has collectors in London, Italy and Australia. Carl has exhibited with Waddington Galleries, Karsten Schubert, Grey Space, Pablo de la Barra, Pino Cassagrande and Alison Jacques at the British School in Rome. He has had solo shows in London, Sydney and Rome.

Recent exhibitions include Fuck Love, his solo show this year in Sydney, Australia.

His up-coming solo show in London, titled Disposable Desire, opens in March 2009 at the Forster Gallery.

TRACEY EMIN

Tracey Emin's art is one of disclosure. Using her life events as inspiration for works ranging from painting, drawing, video and installation to photography, needlework and sculpture, Emin reveals her hopes, humiliations, failures and successes in candid and, at times, excoriating work that is frequently both tragic and humorous.

Emin's work has an immediacy and often sexually provocative attitude.

By reappropriating conventional handicraft techniques for radical intentions, Emin's work resonates with the tenets of the 'personal as political'. In *Everyone I've Ever Slept With*, Emin uses the process of appliqué to inscribe the names of lovers, friends and family within a small tent, into which the viewer has to crawl, thus becoming both voyeur and confidante. Her interest in the work of Edvard Munch and Egon Schiele particularly inform Emin's paintings, monoprints and drawings, which explore complex personal states and ideas of self-representation through manifestly expressionist styles and themes.

JONATHAN YEO

Jonathan Yeo taught himself to paint in his early twenties and carved out a career in the nineties painting pop stars, royalty and Russian mafiosi. He became a big noise in portraiture, receiving commissions from the likes of Erin O' Connor, David Walliams, Grayson Perry, Tony Blair and Nicole Kidman. In the noughties Yeo kept up his notoriety by flouting the rules. In 2001 he unveiled a triptych of Blair, Hague and Kennedy whose varying sizes acted as popularity barometers. In 2002 his photorealist paintings for Theo Fennell were pulled from US magazines for their graphic nudity. The next year he caused controversy at the Royal Society of Portrait Painters by dropping the curtain on a full-frontal nude double portrait of Ivan Massow.

In 2007, after toing and froing with the Dubya Bush camp over a portrait of their leader, Yeo decided to do his own version – a collage of the President of the United States made from pieces of hard-core porn. Bush's furrowed brow is a mishmash of writhing naked flesh while his ear is a ripped-up finger-flick to the laws of the land (showing a sexual act reportedly illegal in the state of Texas). From this, came Blue Period, a show of pornographic images of celebrities, artists and nudes. Yeo gained widespread recognition for a controversial portrait of Tony Blair with a blood-red poppy in 2007 and commissions from the world's glitterati continue to flood in.

Opinions on the route Yeo follows are divided. The National Portrait Gallery describes Yeo's work as a combination of 'photographic realism and a painterly touch', Dennis Hopper describes it as 'timeless and exquisite', and the US Republican party calls it 'extremely distasteful'.

The piece in this book is also in collage, but in a more subtle way. The delicate autumn leaves in the picture reveal, on closer inspection, a multitude of sins.

SAM TAYLOR-WOOD

Sam Taylor-Wood makes photographs and films that explore, through highly charged scenarios, our shared social and psychological conditions.

Taylor-Wood's work examines the split between being and appearance, often placing her human subjects – either singly or in groups – in situations where the line between interior and external sense of self is in conflict. Her languid and silent film portrait of David Beckham, for example, which was shot in a single take, offers a serene alternative to this most intensively photographed celebrity. In *Prelude in Air* (2006) Taylor-Wood filmed a musician playing a piece of cello music by Bach, but the cello itself has been erased. Likewise, in *Breach (Girl and Eunuch)* (2001) a girl is portrayed sitting on the floor in the throes of grief, but the sound of her tears has been removed. In the celebrated film *Still Life* (2001), an impossibly beautiful bowl of fruit decays at an accelerated pace, creating a visceral *memento mori*. Taylor-Wood has also explored notions of weight and gravity in elegiac, poised photographs and films such as *Ascension* (2003) and a series of self-portraits (*Self Portrait Suspended I–VIII*) that depict the artist floating in mid air without the aid of any visible support. In her film *The Last Century* (2006), what appears to be a static image of a group of people slowly reveals itself to be a real, filmed take, timed to the length of a burning cigarette: the film is entirely static apart from the involuntary blinking, twitching and barely visible breathing of four motionless actors, all arranged around a central figure as if in a group portrait painted by Rembrandt or Caravaggio. Recently, Taylor-Wood directed her first narrative short film, *Love You More* (2008), with a script by Patrick Marber.

Sam Taylor-Wood was born in London in 1967 and has had numerous group and solo exhibitions, including the Venice Biennale (1997) and the Turner Prize (1998). Solo exhibitions include Kunsthalle Zurich (1997), Louisiana Museum of Modern Art, Humlebaek (1997), Hirshhorn Museum and Sculpture Garden, Washington DC (1999), Museo Nacional Centro de Arte Reina Sofia, Madrid (2000), the

135

Hayward Gallery, London (2002), the State Russian Museum, St Petersburg (2004), MCA, Moscow (2004), BALTIC, Gateshead (2006), MCA, Sydney (2006), MoCA, Cleveland (2007) and the Contemporary Art Museum, Houston (2007).

MINHO KWON

Minho Kwon was born in Seoul, South Korea in 1979. He originally studied Graphic Design at Kyoungwon University on a scholarship (1998), focusing mainly on typography and illustration (while also working as an assistant drawing tutor for a private art institute for high-school students). In his second year he was enrolled for military service (2000) and spent the next two years serving as a handyman and carpenter. In 2002 he arrived in the UK and embarked on the Graphic Design course at Central Saint Martins College of Art and Design, graduating in 2007. Minho was a Jerwood National Drawing Prize winner (2007) and is currently exhibiting around the country.

Selected group exhibitions include:

Discipline, Brick Lane, London (2006), Hutch Aqffin Gallery (2007), Work in Progress, Elm Lester Painting Rooms, London (2007), Central Saint Martins Degree Show (2007) and the Jerwood Drawing Prize UK touring exhibition (2007).

TIM NOBLE AND SUE WEBSTER

Tim Noble and Sue Webster are known for magically transforming garbage into art. They sculpt piles of street rubbish, studio debris and taxidermic animals into astonishing representations of life, with 'real' shadows of the artists themselves hovering over their accumulations of discarded objects. These abstract forms mysteriously reverse the abstraction into figuration.

Noble & Webster have created a remarkable group of anti-monuments in their twelve-year career, mixing the strategies of modern sculpture and the attitude of punk to make art from anti-art. Their work derives much of its power from its fusion of opposites, form and anti-form, high culture and anti-culture, male and female, craft and rubbish, sex and violence. It is an art of magic and illusion, but it is also an art of direct experience; by combining elements of sculpture, advertising and the persona, the artists have succeeded in making their lives and the experience of the viewer part of the art.

In 2007, Noble & Webster were awarded the ARKEN Prize at Arken Museum of Modern Art, Copenhagen, for their outstanding contribution to the international scene of contemporary art, and their critically acclaimed site-specific project Polymorphous Perverse at the Freud Museum, which included the works Scarlett and Black Narcissus, 2006, was nominated for the prestigious South Bank Prize.

Their first public art installation, Electric Fountain, was unveiled at Rockefeller Plaza, New York, in February 2008.

RACHEL HOWARD

Rachel Howard is a painter. Born in Easington, Co. Durham, at eighteen she moved to London to go to Goldsmiths' College to study Fine Art. In the past two years she has had solo exhibitions at Gagosian Gallery, Los Angeles; Bohen Foundation, New York; Haunch of Venison, London; and the Museum van Loon, Amsterdam. She lives and works in London and Gloucestershire.

JOHN MAYBURY

A painter, writer and director, John Maybury began his cinematographic career shooting films in and around London's punk scene. Collaborations with the seminal British film maker Derek Jarman include *Jubilee* (1977), *Last of England* (1987) and *War Requiem* (1988).

In 1992, BBC films and the actress Tilda Swinton approached Maybury to adapt Manfred Karge's play *Man to Man* for the screen. The resulting film received the International Critics' Prize at the Edinburgh Film Festival.

Maybury's film *Remembrance of Things Fast*, starring Tilda Swinton and Rupert Everett, won the Los Angeles Critics' Circle Award for the Best Independent / Experimental Film of 1994, the Golden Jury Teddy Bear (Berlin Film Festival) and Best Experimental Film (Viper Film Festival, Zurich). It also went on to garner more complaints on being screened on television than any other film in Channel 4's history up to that point.

While sustaining a career as a film and video artist, along with staging numerous international painting exhibitions, Maybury also directed promotional videos for major recording artists, including the Smiths, the Jesus and Mary Chain, Cyndi Lauper, Boy George, Marc Almond, Neneh Cherry and Morrissey. He worked most prolifically with Sinead O'Connor, with the video for her hit single 'Nothing Compares 2 U' being nominated for a Grammy and winning three major MTV awards, including Best Video.

Maybury has created video installations as environments for live performances including the fashion shows of designers Rifat Ozbek and Alexander McQueen,

the Glyndebourne Opera and the world tours of musicians Psychic TV, Kylie Minogue and U2.

Maybury is regarded as a pioneer in British contemporary art. Exhibitions include one-man shows at the Institute of Contemporary Arts (London) and the Palazzo dell' Espezzione (Rome), as well as retrospectives in Europe, Japan and the USA. He has participated widely in group exhibitions at major galleries throughout the world, including the Centre Georges Pompidou (Paris), Tate Britain and Tate Modern (London).

In 1998, Maybury made his first feature film, *Love is the Devil*, an examination of the doomed relationship between artist Francis Bacon and his lover George Dyer. The film enjoyed great success at the 1998 Cannes Film Festival, and played to acclaim at festivals around the world, winning various awards including the Michael Powell Award for Best New British Film at the Edinburgh Film Festival as well as Best Actor awards for Sir Derek Jacobi and Daniel Craig.

His dark, disturbing vision of cinema led to a commission from George Clooney and Steven Soderbergh's company, Section 8, to direct *The Jacket* (2005), starring Keira Knightley and Adrien Brody. A controversial psychological thriller, it led on to commissions from HBO in America ('Rome', Season II, Episodes 7 and 10, 2008).

In 2008, Maybury directed *The Edge of Love* (starring Keira Knightly and Sienna Miller), a film based on a brief moment in the life and loves of the poet Dylan Thomas.

Future projects include an examination of the life of the American photographer Lee Miller as writer/director.

Soho has always been central to John's life and work. He has lived near Soho for over twenty years and immortalised the Colony Room Club in *Love is the Devil*, capturing the essence of the infamous drinking club for ever.

ELK

I've known the name Elk since the late eighties when I used to see his silver pieces along the track-sides, high up on the side of a building that could be seen from the Picadilly Line as I headed for Heathrow Airport, or else, incredibly enough, his tags in silver marker inside every doorway of every District Line train on the black rubber panel at your feet on either side . . .

I then began noticing his colour pieces too, knowing full well that this was only the visible side of what he was doing and that a whole load of pieces, especially on the trains, were hidden from me. We had friends in common but I really only got to know him through painting at the sunken playground near Barons Court where he would organise a painting jam called Unity every summer. I don't know how many of these he did get to organise but he commanded such respect from even the most hardcore elements that it enabled him to bring together writers from all over the country and from all levels of legality and illegality . . .

He always has his finger on the pulse of what's going on with the scene and has quite a collection of paraphernalia and mementoes picked up here and there, all to do with the different transport networks that intertwine their way through the European cities . . .

His devotion to the art and the cause

is unwavering as he balances work priorities and his many trips abroad with every chance he can get to paint, still steadily developing his own particular style of looping letters and colours . . .

This attitude has also led him to the world of photography where he would even end up taking a medium-format camera to the most illegal of places and capturing images of a world that you and I will maybe never see . . .

Mode 2

JIM LAMBIE

Jim Lambie was born in 1964 in Glasgow, Scotland, and he graduated from Glasgow School of Art with a BA (Hons) in environmental art. He is a contemporary visual artist and was shortlisted for the 2005 Turner Prize with an installation called Mental Oyster.

Lambie specialises in taking the ephemera of modern life and transforming it into vibrant sculptural installations. Working with items immediately to hand, as well as those sourced in second-hand and hardware stores, he resurrects record decks, speakers, clothing, accessories, doors and mirrors to form sculptural elements in larger compositions. Lambie prioritises sensory pleasure over intellectual response. He selects materials that are familiar and have a strong personal resonance, so that they offer a way into the work as well as a springboard to a psychological space beyond.

Lambie's works are often devised in relation to a specific space, where they are shaped by a series of intuitive and improvisatory decisions. This enables him to work in tune with the qualities of his materials and the parameters of the existing architecture.

PHIL DIRTBOX

Phil Dirtbox has been around Soho and the Soho club scene since the early 1980s and is celebrated for hosting his infamous two-day underground parties. He is a well-known and respected figure in not only Soho but also the West End. He has an amazing talent for poetry which we are fortunate enough to have an example of in this collection. He can often be found outside the French House on

Dean Street bellowing out one of these creations which range from lovely to downright debauched. So, if you can imagine a towering man, nearly seven feet tall, wearing a bowler and a sensationally eccentric suit that would put Joseph with his many colours to shame, you can just about imagine what a fantastic figure he cuts.

P.S. There is even talk on those Soho streets of Phil Dirtbox lampshades being on sale by Halloween (not to put in nurseries).

TONY HUSBAND

Tony Husband is a multi-award-winning cartoonist. His work appears in *The Times*, *Sunday Express*, *Private Eye*, *The Spectator*, *Playboy* and many other publications. He created the cult comic *Oink* and the kids TV series *Round the Bend*. He's working on his own range of greeting cards and calendars and he tours with poet Ian McMillan with their cartoon and poetry event. Tony has had more than thirty books published around the world and he supports Manchester United.

DAMIEN HIRST

Born in Bristol in 1965, Damien Hirst studied at Goldsmiths' College. In 1988 he curated the now renowned exhibition Freeze, held in London. In 1991 he had his first solo exhibition in London entitled In and Out of Love and the following year he was a major contributor to the ground-breaking Young British Artists exhibitions at the Saatchi Gallery. He was awarded the prestigious Turner Prize in 1995. Hirst's work has been shown in many important group and solo shows throughout the world and he is now one of Britain's most celebrated living artists. He lives and works in Devon and London.

PETER BLAKE

Peter Blake was born on 25 June 1932 in Dartford, Kent. Having attended Gravesend School of Art, he went on to the Royal College of Art in London, where he was awarded a First Class Diploma. During the late 1950s, Blake became one of the best known British pop artists. His paintings from this time drew on imagery from advertisements, music-hall entertainment and wrestling, often including collaged elements. Blake took part in group exhibitions at the Institute of Contemporary Arts and had his first solo exhibition in 1960. It was with the Young Contemporaries exhibition of 1961, where he was exhibited alongside David Hockney and R. B. Kitaj, that he was first identified with the emerging British Pop Art movement. Blake won the John Moores Junior Award in 1961 for his work *Self Portrait with Badges*.

Blake designed several notable album sleeves, including *Sgt. Pepper's Lonely Hearts Club Band*, which has become a much imitated iconic work of pop art, as well as sleeves for the Band Aid single, *Do They Know It's Christmas?* (1984), Paul Weller's *Stanley Road* (1995), the Ian Dury tribute album *Brand New Boots and Panties* (2001) and Oasis' greatest-hits album *Stop the Clocks* (2006).

Blake was made a CBE in 1983 and in the same year a major retrospective of his work was held at the Tate Gallery. In 2002 Blake was awarded a knighthood for his services to art. In February 2005, the Sir Peter Blake Music Art Gallery, located in the School of Music, University of Leeds, was opened by the artist; the permanent exhibition features seventeen examples of Blake's album-sleeve art, including the only public showing of a signed print of his famed *Sgt. Pepper's* artwork.

More recently, Blake has created Artist's Editions for the opening of the Pallant House Gallery, which houses collections that include some of his most famous paintings, and in 2008 there was a retrospective of his work in Bilbao and at Tate Liverpool.